Landscapes of Alaska

*Mount McKinley as
viewed from Wonder Lake*

Landscapes of Alaska

Their Geologic Evolution

Prepared by members of the United States Geological Survey
Published in coöperation with the National Park Service,
United States Department of the Interior
Edited by Howel Williams

1958
BERKELEY AND LOS ANGELES
UNIVERSITY OF CALIFORNIA PRESS

Volume I of Part Four—Geology and Geography

of the National Park Service's Recreation

Survey of Alaska

© 1958 BY THE REGENTS OF THE UNIVERSITY OF CALIFORNIA
UNIVERSITY OF CALIFORNIA PRESS
BERKELEY AND LOS ANGELES, CALIFORNIA
CAMBRIDGE UNIVERSITY PRESS
LONDON, ENGLAND
LIBRARY OF CONGRESS CATALOG CARD NUMBER: 58-8655
PRINTED IN THE UNITED STATES OF AMERICA
DESIGNED BY JOHN B. GOETZ

Foreword

The meaning of this book is so eloquently revealed as one reads the first chapter that it needs no explanation here, except for a few words on how it was produced.

During the past decade the National Park Service, in coöperation with Territorial representatives and other authorities, has surveyed and reported on several aspects of the recreation resources of Alaska. When the time came to report on the recreation value of Alaska's scenery—to discuss it penetratingly as a cultural asset important in the economy of the Territory—the United States Geological Survey was asked to help. Such helpfulness has long been traditional with the Survey. The Park Service and the Survey concluded that, since everything in landscape scenery is of the earth, and since our understanding of the physical evolution of Alaska's land forms probably is most clearly in the minds of the Survey's geologists, they should furnish the facts.

"Why not," we said, "ask the geologists to present their knowledge of Alaska's landscapes in such a way that the rest of us can gain a better comprehension of the scene?" We believed that the geologists, as authors, would bring home to the rest of us a better grasp of the Territory's vast scenic resources; and I am sure that the reader will agree that the Geological

Survey authors have appreciably supplemented our visual sense by explaining the meaning of what we see in Alaska. We are indebted to them for the classic manner in which this subject is presented.

We hope that this book will stimulate interest in and appreciation of Alaska's magnificent landscapes.

Conrad L. Wirth, Director
National Park Service

Acknowledgments

This book has come into being through the efforts of many contributors. We conceived it in 1951, and it has evolved in steps and stages to completion in 1958, as help from the most able people in the country was obtained for each part of the undertaking.

Certain individuals and institutions have provided essential help which we gratefully acknowledge. Bradford Washburn, Director, Boston Museum of Science, supplied most of the photographic illustrations. John C. Reed, Staff Coördinator, and George O. Gates, Chief, Alaska Branch, both of the United States Geological Survey, participated in the formulation of ideas for the book and collaborated closely with the authors and producers. Robert L. Moravetz, Chief, Office of Publications in the Geological Survey, exercised unusual technical knowledge in planning and producing the color maps.

The Pan American World Airways System, long of service to Alaska, gave the color picture of Mount McKinley which is used as the frontispiece.

The Goodnews Bay Mining Company, which operates a platinum mine on the coast of the Bering Sea, and the Humble Oil & Refining Company, Union Oil Company of California, the Richfield Oil Company, the Shell Oil

Company, the Ohio Oil Company, and the General Petroleum Corporation, who are engaged in explorations for oil in Alaska, each contributed financially toward the cost of publication.

The University of California Press designed and published the book with, we believe, exceptional understanding and skillful treatment of the subject.

Appreciation and thanks are due all of these special contributors, and to many others who helped in one way or another to produce this book.

George L. Collins, Chief
Alaska Recreation Survey

Contents

INTRODUCTION   1
    by John C. Reed and Howel Williams

SOUTHEASTERN ALASKA   9
    by John C. Reed

GULF OF ALASKA AREA   19
    by Don J. Miller

WRANGELL MOUNTAINS   30
    by Robert F. Black

COPPER RIVER PLATEAU   34
    by Robert F. Black

TALKEETNA MOUNTAINS   38
    by Farrell F. Barnes

COOK INLET–SUSITNA LOWLAND   43
    by Farrell F. Barnes

x   *Contents*

THE ALASKA RANGE   48
    by Clyde Wahrhaftig

ALASKA PENINSULA—ALEUTIAN ISLANDS   61
    by Howard A. Powers

LOWLANDS AND PLAINS OF INTERIOR AND WESTERN ALASKA   76
    by Robert F. Black

INTERIOR HIGHLANDS OF WESTERN ALASKA   82
    by Joseph M. Hoare

INTERIOR HIGHLANDS OF EASTERN ALASKA   88
    by Robert M. Chapman

SEWARD PENINSULA   104
    by J. P. Hopkins and D. M. Hopkins

BROOKS RANGE   111
    by George Gryc

ARCTIC SLOPE   119
    by George Gryc

ISLANDS OF THE BERING SEA   128
    by George M. Flint, Jr.

APPENDIX: GEOLOGIC TIME SCALE   137

GLOSSARY   138

INDEX OF GEOGRAPHICAL NAMES   142

Illustrations

Plates

(*following page 52*)

1. Parts of the St. Elias Range and Malaspina Glacier.
2. Hubbard Glacier entering Disenchantment Bay, Yakutat Bay area.
3. Mount Crillon (12,726 feet) and Brady Glacier.
4. Mount Crillon (12,726 feet) viewed across Johns Hopkins Inlet.
5. Nunatak Fiord, Yakutat Bay.
6. Part of the Chugach Range, including Mount Witherspoon (12,023 feet).
7. Perspective diagram of Upper Cook Inlet area showing setting of Anchorage.
8. Mount Sanford and the Wrangell Mountains.
9. Sourdough Peak in the southern foothills of the Wrangell Mountains.
10. Cliffs of Triassic limestone in the southeastern Wrangell Mountains.
11. Mount McKinley from the northeast.

12. Part of the Alaska Range, including Mount McKinley.
13. Eocene coals and sandstones on Lignite Creek, near Healy.
14. Recessional moraines on the north side of Iliamna volcano.
15. Caldera of Katmai volcano.
16. Head of the Valley of Ten Thousand Smokes.
17. Dacite dome on the south flank of Trident volcano.
18. Shishaldin volcano, Unimak Island.
19. Placer gold mining near Fairbanks.
20. Typical upland terrain, northern Seward Peninsula.
21. Mount Doonerak from Amawk Mountain, Brooks Range.
22. Highest part of the Brooks Range.
23. Polygonal ground and thaw lakes near Skull Cliff, southwest of Barrow.

Maps

facing page

1. Physiographic provinces of Alaska.   4
2. Southeastern Alaska.   12
3. Gulf of Alaska area, Wrangell Mountains, Copper River plateau, Talkeetna Mountains, Cook Inlet and Susitna lowland, and Alaska Range.   20
4. Alaska Peninsula–Aleutian Islands.   68
5. Lowlands and plains of interior and western Alaska; interior highlands of western and eastern Alaska; Seward Peninsula.   76
6. Brooks Range and Arctic Slope.   116

Figures

1. Evolution of Okmok caldera, Umnak Island.   62
2. Present areas occupied by glaciers and by permafrost, and areas formerly covered by glaciers at the time of their maximum spread during the Pleistocene period.   *facing page* 80
3. Development of the Bering Sea Land Bridge.   134

JOHN C. REED AND HOWEL WILLIAMS

Introduction

The recreational attraction of any area is intimately related to its landscape, and this in turn is a reflection of its geologic history. If the relationships are obvious, enjoyment comes at once, both from viewing the landscape and from contemplating the processes by which it was produced. Thus the symmetry of a high-arching natural bridge may do much more than please the eye; it may give fuller pleasure by rousing the mind to thought of the age-long erosion by which it was shaped. Geologic explanations serve to deepen understanding of how scenes have come into being. Niagara, Grand Canyon, Crater Lake, Yosemite, Yellowstone, Mount McKinley, or any other spectacular landscape takes on new meaning when one realizes it to be the last of a long series of changing landscapes, the product of relentless forces acting usually at almost imperceptible rates for millions of years. The thrill of historic insight is then added to esthetic pleasure.

"Beneath and behind all the outward beauty of our lowlands, our uplands, and our highlands," wrote Sir Archibald Geikie, "there lies an inner history which, when revealed, will give to that beauty a fuller significance and an added charm." And it has been well said that whatever withdraws us from the power of our senses; whatever makes the past, the distant, or the future predominate over the present, advances us in the dignity of thinking beings.

1

No page in history can be fully understood without knowledge of the pages that went before; neither can a landscape be properly interpreted without knowledge of its geologic background. The geologist viewing a familiar landscape, sees in his mind's eye other views that made the present landscape possible; an enchanter's wand seems to wave over him and by some strange magic blends the past with the present. Geologic influence operates no less in the sunny fields of the Shenandoah Valley, the mist-shrouded mountains of Puget Sound, and the rocky farmlands of New England, than it does among the ice-clad peaks and erupting volcanoes of Alaska; it is by no means confined to bizarre, unusual, or outstanding scenes, although these have special interest and value for purposes of recreation.

Two things must be emphasized above all else if the evolution of Alaska is to be understood: the immensity of geologic time, and the fleeting character of all landscapes. In the appendix there is presented a table showing in chronologic order the principal eras and periods of geologic time, together with their approximate duration in millions of years. The oldest known rocks in Alaska belong to the Precambrian era; they are, therefore, more than 520 million years of age. And yet, because these rocks were once sediments laid down in the sea, there must be still older rocks, now concealed, from which they were derived. During the long Paleozoic era that followed, from 185 million to about 520 million years ago, the open ocean rolled over most of what is now Alaska, for virtually all of the rocks of that era bear unmistakable signs of having been sediments, lava flows, and volcanic ashes laid down beneath the sea. The records of these ancient times are too fragmentary, however, to permit a clear account. Too many early pages of the story are missing, and many of the pages are too badly torn to decipher.

During the first part of the succeeding Mesozoic era, that is, during the Triassic and Jurassic periods, from about 130 million to 185 million years ago, seas continued to occupy most of Alaska, and enormous outpourings of lava took place from submarine and island volcanoes. The products of these tremendous eruptions, the Nikolai greenstones, are now to be seen widely distributed in the southern part of the Territory.

From about the middle of the Jurassic period onward, strong earth movements affected Alaska. These movements were by no means continuous, nor did they take place everywhere at the same time. But at intervals, now here and then there, the earth's crust was buckled and fractured, producing great arcuate uplifts and intervening troughs. Indeed there is nothing more striking in the geologic structure of Alaska than the arcuate arrangement of its fold-belts. This accounts for the long, majestic curves of its major mountain ranges.

Look at the accompanying map showing the physiographic provinces of Alaska (map 1). Note that except for the Brooks Range, which is slightly convex toward the south, and the Aleutian arc, which is much more so, all of the other mountain ranges are arranged concentrically around the Gulf of Alaska, and are convex toward the north. They look like a succession of advancing waves. The crest of the present Brooks Range coincides roughly with the crest of an original upfold; in other words, this range has stood higher than the adjacent areas ever since it was first elevated from the sea in Jurassic times, about 130 million years ago. But quite the opposite is true of most of the other mountain ranges. Surprising as it may seem, the crest of the gigantic Alaska Range coincides approximately with the deepest part of a huge downfold in the earth's crust, and the impressive Chugach-Kenai-Kodiak mountain chain likewise rises on the site of a major downfold. This is why the youngest Mesozoic rocks of the Alaska Range lie along and near the crest, flanked on the north and south by older rocks that dip inward, beneath them.

The earth is forever in motion. Its crust never ceases to pulsate, responding to gradual and fitful changes underground. Parts of the crust are sometimes elevated by being upfolded into anticlines or into still larger arches, called geanticlines. These upfolded belts may then be wiped out by erosion, or may even change into elongated troughs as adjacent belts in their turn are uplifted. At other times, parts of the crust are raised less by folding than by more or less vertical, bodily uplifts. But no matter how the uplifts are produced, many are accompanied by intrusion into the earth's crust of colossal masses of molten, igneous material. That is why granites are so often found in the cores of mountain ranges, for they result from slow cooling and crystallization, deep beneath the surface, of material that was injected while hot and partly liquid. Some geologists suppose that the parent liquid forms by partial melting of deeply buried rocks; others say that the molten material rises from still greater depths where, owing to release of pressure or accumulation of heat by breakdown of radioactive substances, crystalline material is converted to liquid that then rises toward the surface.

In any event, intrusion of enormous volumes of relatively light, partly molten material tends not only to buoy up adjacent parts of the earth's crust, thus contributing to major uplifts, but also brings about recrystallization and metamorphism of the invaded rocks, and is accompanied sometimes by formation of valuable mineral deposits.

Uplifted belts, once they rise above the sea, are immediately subject to denudation, and debris is carried down from their flanks either into inter-montane troughs, or, more commonly, into adjacent submarine depressions. And as sedimentary debris accumulates in these basins, their floors subside beneath the growing loads. Long-continued sagging thus results in major downwarps or geosynclines. And, in due time, geosynclines, together with their content of sedimentary and volcanic rocks, may be buckled and frac-tured by earth movements, and their bottoms may be partly melted to yield batholithic intrusions of granite. And so the former troughs become new fold-mountain ranges with granite cores. Then these in turn are attacked by erosion and their waste returns to the sea whence it came. The cycle starts anew, for the sea is both the grave and birthplace of mountains.

Our images of the ancient seascapes and landscapes of Alaska become less blurred as increasing evidence brings them into sharper focus. About 140 million years ago, during the latter part of the Jurassic period, the an-cestral Brooks Range first rose from the sea. At the same time, the Seward Peninsula was uplifted, as was most of south and southeast Alaska, and in many places these uplifts were due to folding and intrusion of granite batholiths. But already before the Jurassic period had come to an end, some of the resultant mountains, for instance the ancestral Talkeetna Mountains, had been worn down below sea level.

During early Cretaceous time, between 100 million and 130 million years ago, parts of the present Arctic Slope emerged from the sea, although most of it remained submerged. At the same time, parts of interior and southern Alaska were occupied by the sea, and lavas and ashes accumulated there between layers of marine sediment. Then began a long interval of intense deformation, lasting throughout most of mid-Cretaceous time, when the whole of Alaska, from the Brooks Range southward to the Coast Range, was subjected to strong earth movements, and over vast areas folding and faulting were accompanied and followed by renewed injection of large batholiths with consequent metamorphism of the invaded rocks and forma-tion of new mineral veins.

Once more, however, the elevated regions were attacked by erosion. Sedi-ments carried by streams from the Brooks Range and Seward Peninsula were deposited in adjoining seaways, one to the north, on the present site of the Arctic Slope, and another to the south, the Koyukuk geosyncline. On the present sites of the Alaska Range, Nutzotin Mountains, and Mata-nuska Valley, sediments were deposited in lakes and in stream channels while peat accumulated in marshes, later to be converted into the coals of the Cantwell formation. Subsequently, about the close of mid-Cretaceous time, the site of the Alaska Range was again deformed by folding on a large scale. This deformation, however, was not the one responsible for the present height and form of the range; indeed the summits of the mid-Cretaceous Alaska Range generally lay north and south of the present crest, which then was relatively low. Erosion and repeated uplifts during post-Cretaceous times account for the transformation.

During late Cretaceous time, from about 60 million years to 80 million years ago, seas continued to inundate most of the Arctic Slope, and volcanic eruptions contributed layers of ash to the marine sediments that accumulated there. Seas were also present in parts of interior Alaska, and they continued to occupy the present site of the Chugach-Kenai-Kodiak mountain chain. On the other hand, the Seward Peninsula, and the Brooks, Alaska, and Coast ranges stood high, and fluviatile sediments accumulated on their flanks while adjacent volcanoes erupted lava and ash.

Widespread uplifts marked the close of the Cretaceous period. The sediments that had long been piling up within the marine trough on the present site of the Chugach-Kenai-Kodiak chain were folded and raised above the sea. Uplifts were so general that at the dawn of the Tertiary era virtually the whole of Alaska except the fringes stood above sea level.

The Eocene period, between 40 million years and 60 million years ago, was one of extensive volcanic activity. It was then, for instance, that many of the lava flows of the Wrangell Mountains were erupted. It was also a time when stream- and lake-sediments accumulated in large and widely scattered intermontane basins, and when vast peat swamps were prevalent, such as those that gave rise to the coal deposits on the north side of the Alaska Range and those in the Cook Inlet–Susitna Lowlands. The climate was warm temperate to almost subtropical, so that Metasequoia trees flourished as far north as the Arctic Slope.

Renewed earth movements took place during the Eocene period. Parts of interior Alaska, the Alaska Range, and lands bordering the Gulf of Alaska were especially affected, and the movements there were once more accompanied by intrusions of granite and by mineralization. And yet before the start of the succeeding Oligocene period, the newly elevated regions had already been reduced by erosion almost to sea level. It seems likely that the landscape of Alaska was never more subdued or uniform than it was during Oligocene time.

Throughout the succeeding Miocene and Pliocene epochs, that is, from one million years to thirty million years ago, the extent of Alaska was not much different from what it is today, only part of the Arctic Slope around Barrow and some of the present coastal lands fringing the Gulf of Alaska being submerged beneath the sea. Volcanoes were numerous and widespread, especially in the Seward Peninsula, in the interior of Alaska, in the Wrangell and St. Elias ranges, in the Matanuska Valley, in the Alaska Peninsula, and in the Aleutian Chain. Intermittent uplifts accompanied the volcanism, reaching a maximum about the close of the Pliocene period and the beginning of the succeeding Quaternary era. The eastern end of the Arctic Slope, and the Brooks, Alaska, Chugach, and Coast ranges were probably uplifted most; in fact, the Chugach Range rose so high that already in Pliocene time glaciers covered its higher slopes.

The climate of Alaska had been growing cooler throughout the Tertiary era. Ultimately, about a million years ago, the Ice Age began. Glaciers waxed and waned, retreating during warm interglacial spells and then expanding again. When they were largest, almost all of the high ranges were buried completely by gigantic sheets of ice. Long tongues moved down the mountain valleys, coalescing below into colossal piedmont glaciers many of which spread far out to sea, just as the ice sheets of Antarctica do today (see map 1). How these enormous glaciers sculptured the landscape, and how, as they retreated, they left in their wake moraines and outwash plains dotted with countless lakes, is told in the contributions that follow. The principal ranges and valleys of Alaska were already in existence before the Ice Age, but the rugged carving of the mountains and the detailed modeling of the lowlands are mainly the work of glaciers during the last million years.

Volcanoes erupted intermittently throughout the Ice Age, but they were not as widely scattered as those of Tertiary time. Extensive outpourings of basaltic lava continued in the Seward Peninsula, but most of the volcanoes were concentrated in those parts of Alaska where they are still most numerous, that is, in the Alaska Peninsula and in the Aleutian Chain. During the Ice Age also most of the principal mountain ranges were uplifted, and some of them, such as the St. Elias Range, still continue to rise. The signs of these recent uplifts are graphically recorded by wave-cut marine terraces high above the present sea level.

A final word. Alaska was the gateway through which man entered North America. To the archaeologist is left the fascinating task of determining just when the first immigrants arrived, but already it is known that they crossed from Siberia toward the close of the Ice Age, when, owing to the lowering of sea level consequent upon growth of the glaciers, the Bering Strait became dry land (see fig. 3, p. 134).

Such, in briefest outline, is the geologic history of Alaska. The aim of this book is to discuss in more detail such parts of the history as bear most closely on the evolution of the Alaskan landscape. Alaska is indeed a scenic wonderland. It has lakes, rolling plains with magnificent distances, rugged mountains with snowy crags overlooking sheltered alpine valleys, glistening glaciers, and steaming volcanoes, all in bountiful profusion. Here is Mount McKinley, its top 20,300 feet above the sea, the highest peak on the continent. Southwest from the mainland extend the Alaska Peninsula and Aleutian Chain, stretching 1,500 miles across 32 degrees of longitude to Asia, and studded with more than eighty volcanoes. In southeast Alaska the "Inside Passage" winds among rocky wooded islands and through deep, ice-scoured fiords. In the far north, beyond the Arctic Circle, an apparently limitless coastal plain, with perennially frozen subsurface and myriads of lakes, slopes gently to the polar ocean.

Because landscapes reflect the character and distribution of the underlying rocks and the geologic processes active in their sculpture, it follows that regions with different landforms are also regions of different geologic evolution. For that reason, the Territory is first divided for description into four principal regions, namely, the Pacific mountain system, interior and western Alaska, the Brooks Range, and the Arctic Slope. These regions are then subdivided into fourteen smaller areas, as shown in the accompanying map (map 1).

Each of the four principal regions mentioned above has distinctive characteristics. The sweeping arc of the Pacific mountain system defines the Pacific border of Alaska, rising as a giant barrier between the ocean and the broad interior and western Alaska region. To the north lies the little-known Brooks Range, an immense series of rugged highlands that forms the northwestern extension of the Rocky Mountain system of the western United States and Canada. Still farther north stretches the tundra of the Arctic Slope. The characteristic geologic and topographic features of each of these regions have of course exerted a powerful influence on, in fact have largely controlled other features of, the natural environments—their climate, vegetation, accessibility, inhabitants, industry, and development.

In describing the above-mentioned areas, each author, though giving a general account of his terrain, has emphasized one or more features of special prominence. Thus glaciation is stressed in southeastern Alaska, volcanism in the Alaska Peninsula and the Aleutian Islands, and mineral deposits and mining in some of the interior areas.

For some sixty years, the U.S. Geological Survey has been investigating and appraising the mineral resources of Alaska. And because these resources, like most other natural features, are basically related to the geology, this long, systematic effort has been primarily one of studying geologic environments. Accomplishment of this staggering task has required training a corps of specialists collectively acquainted with all parts of the Territory. This corps is now in its second and third generation. Gone from the Territory are the famed early geologists—Alfred H. Brooks, Walter C. Mendenhall, Fred H. Moffit, Philip S. Smith, Stephen R. Capps, and many others. No longer do the trackless forests echo the sound of their axes or rivers reflect the passing of their Peterborough canoes. In their place the modern geologist travels with relative ease and much faster by plane, helicopter, and "weasel"; he grasps much of the regional picture from direct air observations, and he checks and extends his ground studies by interpretation of air photographs by new photogeologic methods.

This modern group of specialists has pooled its familiarity with Alaska to prepare what follows. For the most part, persons were chosen who have had long and specialized experience in the region about which they write. The various contributions have been influenced of course by the individual interests of the authors, but an attempt has been made to achieve a balanced whole, to include features that can be easily appreciated by nongeological readers, and to give a properly proportioned impression of the geologic background.

And so, here is Alaska—vacationland unparalleled—its mountains, rivers, glaciers, fog-swept shores, limitless tundra; land of the sourdough, Eskimo, and Indian; but also land of budding industries, great military bases, networks of airlines, and crossroad to the Orient.

JOHN C. REED

Southeastern Alaska

Southeastern Alaska with its scenic beauty, abundant wildlife, varied eth-
nologic groups, and historical heritage is replete with interest for the casual
tourist, student, businessman, and sportsman. This is Alaska's fabled panhandle, about 125 miles wide, extending from Dixon Entrance northwest to
Skagway, historic gateway to the gold fields of Klondike (see map 2). It is
part of the Pacific mountain system. On the east rise the wind-swept and
snow- and ice-clad peaks of the mighty Coast Range where the international
boundary runs its jagged course along the crest, northwest and then southwest until it angles sharply northwest again at the frosty top of Mount
Fairweather, more than 15,000 feet above the nearby sea. From the crest
of the range, the summit altitudes decrease southwestward, though even
close to the deeply indented edge of the mainland the tops tower 2,000 to
4,000 feet above huge trenchlike valleys. Here is the storied "Inside Passage" where ocean vessels ply deep-water channels between dark-green,
timbered slopes.

Still farther southwest lie the myriad islands of the Alexander Archipelago. These islands, though generally a little lower than the mainland,
are otherwise quite similar, being separated only by narrow fiords, flooded
counterparts of the mainland valleys. The very names of the islands recall

much of the historic background of this maritime province—Revillagigedo, Prince of Wales, Mitkof, Zarembo, Kupreanof, Kuiu, Baranof, Chichagof, and Admiralty.

Most of the larger streams of the mainland issue from glaciers that funnel down valleys from the higher parts of the Coast Range. Some glaciers extend clear to the heads of the fiords where they discharge great icebergs into the sea as 20-foot tides agitate their fronts. Other glaciers descend only part way to the sea before melting balances advance; milky rivers then carry their silty meltwaters through braided channels to the coast. During the tourist season, steamers sometimes diverge from their courses to give passengers a view of one or more of these tidewater glaciers, such as the Taku, and smaller boats safely approach many others, including those in Glacier Bay, and in Endicott and Tracy arms. Or again a short drive by good highway from Juneau leads to the terminus of the magnificent Mendenhall Glacier, which once extended to the sea but has now retreated far enough to permit the Juneau airport to be built on its outwash plain.

Areas of subdued relief are uncommon in southeastern Alaska. Below the jagged higher peaks along some of the major, and many of the minor, divides there are somewhat less rugged uplands. There are in addition a very few flat and gently rolling areas of substantial extent near sea level, some of which consist of unconsolidated glacial deposits, either water-transported materials or ice-formed moraines. Such an area has already been mentioned as including the Juneau airport. Another is the Point Agassiz area north of Petersburg, and still another lies east of the mouth of Glacier Bay, where the Gustavus airport has been built. Some relatively gentle areas, on the other hand, are underlain by hard rock with little or no cover of unconsolidated material. One such area on Annette Island was chosen just before World War II as the site of the Annette airport that now serves Ketchikan; another covers a substantial tract along the west side of Yakobi Island and part of Chichagof Island; a third comprises the Mansfield Peninsula at the north end of Admiralty Island, terminating at Point Retreat, a familiar landmark to sailors in these waters.

Less conspicuous features of southeastern Alaska are the old beaches that extend at various elevations up to several hundred feet above present sea level. These old beaches are not everywhere horizontal; hence they cannot have been produced simply by lowering of the ocean or by uniform uplift of the land, but must have resulted from differential upwarping of the coast.

The bedrocks of southeastern Alaska vary widely in origin, kind, and age, but two generalities apply to most of them and are important in understanding the evolution of the landscape: (1) they were once buried deeply in the earth's crust, were then uplifted, and have been exposed by deep erosion and removal of the rocks that originally covered them; (2) they have a grain or banding that generally dips steeply and trends almost parallel to the long axis of the Alaskan panhandle. Before describing the rocks in detail, however, attention must be called to the colossal, straight trench occupied by Chatham Strait and Lynn Canal, stretching south and a little east from near Skagway to a line between the southern tips of Baranof and Kuiu islands. Because the rocks and structures on opposite sides of this extraordinary trench do not match, it is believed to mark the trace of a great fault or break in the earth's crust. Beyond Skagway, the fault continues northwestward and then westward in a gigantic arc through parts of British Columbia and Yukon Territory and thence along the full length of the Alaska Range, as described in a later contribution. Thus Chatham Strait and Lynn Canal set apart the large outer islands of Baranof and Chichagof and the Glacier Bay country from the rest of southeastern Alaska.

To the east of this great fault lies the Coast Range batholith, a truly stupendous body of granitic rocks formed from intrusions of molten igneous material that slowly cooled and crystallized far beneath the surface while hot liquids and vapors issuing from them altered the surrounding rocks. Scattered throughout this huge granitic batholith are foundered remnants of the roof and countless fragments torn from the walls when the molten material was slowly injected. Large and small offshoots of the Coast Range batholith are prevalent though not predominant in all other belts of southeastern Alaska, except in the belt of Tertiary rocks to be mentioned later.

Southwest of the main batholith is a belt of metamorphic and sedimentary rocks, including gneisses, schists, marbles, phyllites, and slates. This belt embraces the rest of the mainland, except the part west of Lynn Canal, most of Admiralty, more than half of Kupreanof and Zarembo, and all of Etolin and Revillagigedo islands. The rocks here are of Paleozoic and Mesozoic age, and most of them were profoundly altered by intrusion of the batholith during Cretaceous time.

A third belt includes the southwest part of Admiralty Island and Kupreanof and Kuiu islands, as well as the west part of Zarembo Island. This belt consists of younger rocks, of Tertiary age, among them being sedimentary rocks, including a little coal on Admiralty Island, and also andesitic and rhyolitic lavas and related volcanic deposits. This belt ends abruptly at

Chatham Strait but reappears farther west along the coast of the Gulf of Alaska.

Another belt of sedimentary and volcanic rocks, but of Paleozoic age, lies still farther southwest, including most of Kuiu and all of Prince of Wales Island and adjacent islands. This also ends on the west against the great fiord of Lynn Canal and Chatham Strait.

West of the fiord are two more major belts. One of them, which embraces most of the Glacier Bay area and the northeast part of Chichagof Island to about the head of Port Frederick, is similar in some ways to the Prince of Wales belt just mentioned; the other, which lies to the southwest and includes the rest of Chichagof and most of Baranof Island, is composed mostly of greenstones and graywackes of Mesozoic age.

These, then, are the major units in the framework of southeastern Alaska, and within them, as noted already, the banding and bedding of the rocks generally dip steeply, trending approximately northwest-southeast, roughly parallel to the length of the panhandle.

Concerning the early geologic history of southeastern Alaska, it is intended only to glean a few points that will be helpful in understanding the present landscape. During Paleozoic time, from about 185 million years to 520 million years ago, most, if not all of the area, was under the sea, for there are widespread marine sedimentary rocks, such as limestones, shales, and graywackes, of that age. During the succeeding Mesozoic era, between 60 million years and 185 million years ago, seas continued to occupy the area, and eruptions took place on a stupendous scale, from submarine and island volcanoes, as shown by the presence of thick and extensive sheets of greenstones, originally lava flows and ashes, between layers of marine sedimentary rocks.

Then, in Cretaceous time, the Coast Range batholith and its offshoots were introduced. These intrusions were accompanied, perhaps in part were caused, by tremendous crustal compression that folded and sheared the older rocks. The molten batholithic material was emplaced gradually, far beneath the surface, and it heated and permeated the enclosing rocks, greatly changing their appearance.

In Tertiary time a large downwarp developed, forming a trough into which poured the lava flows of the belt of Tertiary rocks already mentioned. Renewed earth movements then took place, one effect being to produce the great fault now marked by the spectacular fiord of Lynn Canal and Chatham Strait.

Thus was prepared the land that was sculptured during Pleistocene and

Recent times, that is, during the last million years, into the landscape one sees today. This was the gigantic block from which the frigid fingers of ice sheets carved the amazing jumble of peaks, rounded shoulders, and tremendous furrows that make up the Totemland of the Haidas, Tlingits, and Chilkats.

The land was probably high when the Ice Age began, but its precise topography is unknown. Probably then, as now, the mountains formed a barrier to warm, moisture-laden winds blowing in from the broad Pacific. As the winds were deflected upward by the barrier, they were cooled and dropped their load of moisture, sometimes as rain and sometimes as snow, before they passed on to the east. The snow gradually compacted to bodies of ice that grew large enough to move down the valleys as glaciers. Amphitheater-shaped cirques were formed at the valley heads as the glaciers filed and gnawed at the rocky barricades. Detritus ground from the valley bottoms and spalled from the valley walls by wind and frost was carried down in the ice to provide powerful, abrasive tools.

This, however, was only a beginning. The glaciers continued to expand as the climate became wetter and cooler. Ice fields near the divides started to coalesce; valley glaciers grew larger and many tongues reached clear to the sea. Wherever possible the flow of the ice was controlled by the northwest-southeast trending grain of the underlying rocks, but generally the slope of the ice sheets was across the grain and most of the cutting was that way too.

But the climax was not yet reached. Southeastern Alaska had become an icy land indeed; even valley glaciers spilled over their confining walls so that a great sloping sheet of ice completely buried the region, islands and all, and extended many miles out over the ocean as a huge ice shelf, like the shelves that now fringe the ice cap of Antarctica. Meanwhile, the ice ground relentlessly at the underlying surface, buffing off peaks and cliffs, rounding and subduing the whole, and where the ice was especially thick or its flow was concentrated, it gouged still deeper, in places even below present sea level. At this glacial maximum, only jagged pinnacles in the higher parts of the Coast Range rose above the mantle of ice.

As time went on, climate or possibly other factors changed slightly. Very slowly, the ice began to recede. First it retreated landward to the shore and then farther inland and upward. Perhaps the ice disappeared entirely, but if so, conditions changed again and it advanced once more, overriding and destroying forests that had become reëstablished. Several fluctuations took place. All that now survives of the immense sheets of ice are remnants among the higher ranges and a few smaller icefields elsewhere, as on Baranof Island. Valley glaciers still push down from these, and some still reach the sea where icebergs tumble from their snouts and drift with the currents, to be grounded on beaches or gradually to disintegrate in the warmer water and warm summer air.

In very recent time there has been a general retreat of the ice. This has been observed directly, and is clearly shown by zones of sparse vegetation, or of new growth only, close to the ice fronts. Advance of forests into uncovered areas has lagged behind the receding ice.

Two other geologic phenomena must be mentioned to complete the story. One is volcanism; the other, mountain building. Recent lava flows have been recognized at several places in southeastern Alaska, but most of them are in relatively isolated areas, some deep in the mainland ranges. The most conspicuous evidences of recent volcanism are the craters on Kruzof Island on the outer coast off Sitka, and on Baranof Island. The most striking of these volcanoes is Mount Edgecumbe. Indeed so recent is this beautifully symmetrical cone that the legend of its eruptions is said to be still recognizable in native lore. Flows from the vent are plainly to be seen, and ash from the crater covers a wide area to the north and east of Chichagof and Baranof islands, lying on top of, and hence being younger than, the glacial moraines.

At the northern end of southeastern Alaska is the Fairweather Range, a part of the St. Elias Mountains. It towers above the other coastal mountains, culminating in Mount Fairweather itself, more than 15,000 feet above the sea. Apparently the range is still rising at a surprisingly rapid rate. On its flanks, many hundreds of feet above sea level, are beach deposits, containing Recent fossils. Earthquakes, which are rather common in the area, result from continued upward movements of parts of the range.

With the foregoing geologic history in mind, one can interpret and therefore appreciate better many of the natural features of southeastern Alaska as one sails in comfort through the beautiful "Inside Passage" or rapidly wings up the coast in a plane. Some of these features of modern Totemland may now be sampled.

As the north-bound plane from Seattle circles for its first landing in Alaska on the Annette Island airfield near Ketchikan, the pilot is likely to swing over the southern end of Clarence Strait, an imposing, straight-walled waterway, the trench of a great glacier, long since receded, and now partly flooded by the sea. As the plane dips over Gravina Island, rounded summits and shoulders of low mountains appear; these were overridden by the all-enveloping ice sheet at its maximum flood. Soon the plane passes low over Metlakahtla, and a small lake nestling in the mountains to the east comes into view. It is a typical cirque-lake cut by a small vanished glacier, once tributary to the larger ice stream that occupied Nichols Passage and joined the great Clarence Strait Glacier. The valley of this little glacier, like that of many other valley glaciers, descends by large steps so that the lake lies substantially above the lowland and so supplies both water and power to the village. Approaching the field, the plane skims a broad flattish bench cut by the sea when it stood higher than at present. From this bench there project a few low, rounded knobs of a bright orange tint, composed of ultrabasic material, a variant of the rocks composing the Coast Range batholith. This rock contains chromite, but not in sufficient quantities to be of economic value.

Now let the visitor transfer to the deck of a small power boat plying the milky water of Tracy Arm which deeply indents the Coast Range not far south of Juneau. By this time, he can easily recognize that he is in a typical fiord, formerly carved by a powerful glacier. The steep, straight sides; the U-shaped cross section; the nearly horizontal ice-carved flutings on the walls: all are typical. The milky water and the green and blue floating icebergs indicate that a remnant glacier still debouches into the head of the fiord. A glance at the pilothouse chart shows the astonishing depth to which the earlier glacier ground its floor. Still more impressive are the views above the confining walls, hundreds and in places thousands of feet high, to the rounded uplands. Even the colossal trench of the fiord was only a minor channel beneath the great sea of ice that overrode the surrounding summits. Occasionally the passenger catches glimpses far to the east of the jagged peaks of the Coast Range in their snowy mantles and skirted with ice. These peaks were never completely overwhelmed, even at the greatest stand of the ice, and hence were never subdued and rounded by glacial scour.

The rather light-colored granitic rock of the main batholith is well exposed in the walls of the fiord; in sharp contrast are shreds, fragments, and larger masses of older rocks that formed the walls and roof of the batholith. Near the entrance to the arm, high on the east wall, are a few beds of prebatholithic rocks that were heated and permeated by emanations until they were changed locally to masses of sulfide minerals containing zinc, lead, and silver ores.

At Juneau, the capital city, a glacial valley, now occupied by Gold Creek, debouches into Gastineau Channel, a fiord between the mainland and

Douglas Island. Not far above the town, the creek has incised its bed below the floor of the old glacial valley, so that its narrow steep gorge gives a measure both of the time that has elapsed since the valley was filled with ice and of the eroding power of the postglacial stream. The headward parts of the valley are carved in the main Coast Range batholith. Farther downstream the valley passes into the wall rocks of the batholith, and for several hundreds of feet above the contact these rocks are transected by a network of small quartz veins containing gold and other metallic minerals. These too were produced by emanations from the batholith, and collectively they form the famous Alaska Juneau ore body which has yielded many millions of dollars worth of the precious yellow metal. The loose, postglacial material in the valley on and below the Juneau lode contains placer gold. Indeed, this is one of the few such deposits in southeastern Alaska, for in most places glaciers have removed any older deposits that may have been present, and there has not been enough time since the ice retreated to allow new ones to accumulate.

Next suppose the traveler leaves Juneau by small craft. The boat runs down Gastineau Channel, rounds Marmion Island at the southern tip of Douglas Island into Stephens Passage, a still larger fiord, and turns westward into the great trench of Chatham Strait down which it proceeds southward and again westward into Icy Strait. Soon the boat approaches the broad entrance to Glacier Bay and turns northward through bewildering tide currents that run over the shoal entrance to the heart of the Glacier Bay National Monument. On either side are stretches of flat land unusual in southeastern Alaska, and on the flat to the east is built the large Gustavus airport. These flat areas, as well as the low Beardslee Islands north of the entrance to the bay, are composed of moraine and outwash material from the great glacier that once filled Glacier Bay. During the past few hundred years the ice has receded rapidly and divided into many branches that still discharge 'bergs into the headward branches of the bay.

This magnificent glacial environment in the shadow of the lofty Fairweather Range is an unsurpassed field laboratory for study and appreciation of glaciation and for investigation of biological, botanical, and many other natural subjects. On some beaches several layers of interglacial forests are exposed. Near the present ice fronts, vegetation is nearly lacking, not having had time to reëstablish itself after recession of the ice. In impressive expanse are displayed the mature forest near the entrance, grading northward into new conifer forest, then alder and willow thickets, then prostrate varieties of such plants as willows, and finally into bare rock, ice, and glacial moraine.

The fortunate and rugged visitor may be able to go ashore close to the imposing ice cliff at the face of a tidewater glacier and make his way farther up the ice-filled valley observing tributary valleys, filled at their lower ends with large milky lakes dammed by the glacier and moraines. Above the shore he may see old beach lines formed before the lake levels were lowered as water broke out by failure of icy dams.

Again the traveler may leave Juneau for a swing around part of southeastern Alaska in a small amphibious aircraft. The plane climbs rapidly, to 5,000 feet. Below, to the east, is the main Coast Range still almost covered by a large ice cap, looking much as it did at a more advanced stage of glaciation, and still feeding great tongues of ice that push far down the valleys. Below is the beautiful Mendenhall Glacier almost touched by the Glacier Highway from Juneau. Its snout is buried in Mendenhall Lake, and a little farther west is the older Auke Lake. Near Gastineau Channel is the Juneau airport built on the outwash plain from the glacier. The plane turns westward across Lynn Canal and a high peninsula and the whole panorama of Glacier Bay appears. Westward the plane goes until it seems it may strike the white wall of Mount Fairweather towering 2 miles higher.

Finally the plane banks to the south and starts up the northward-flowing Lamplugh Glacier. Although the plane keeps at about 5,000 feet, the glacier below seems to come closer until it is only about 2,000 feet below in a vast ice field supplied largely from the Fairweather Range to the west. Then the plane crosses the end of Brady Glacier, where the ice founders in a mud flat near the head of Taylor Bay; a few minutes later, it flies through the passes leading from the Gulf of Alaska through the Inian Islands into Icy Strait and is over Lisianski Inlet and Chichagof Island. A few sharp peaks rise above the country rounded by the ice. Through an abandoned glacial trough on Yakobi Island one sees to the west a coastal plain several miles wide; this is a surface, with only a thin veneer of morainal material, cut by the sea when it was at a higher level than it is now. Near the divide of Yakobi Island one also sees the dark brown-stained nickel-bearing rocks of the Bohemia Basin, part of the Coast Range batholith.

A little farther south, the old mine workings of Chichagof and Hirst-Chichagof come into view. Traces of myriads of faults can be seen cutting graywackes and greenstones of Cretaceous age. These form the loci of gold-bearing quartz veins produced by emanations from intrusions related to the batholith. Far ahead and a little to starboard rises the majestic cone of Mount Edgecumbe, source of the vast blanket of ash that was spread over the whole area shortly after the ice retreated. As the plane approaches the volcano, one sees recent lava flows that poured down the flanks into the sea.

The plane lands briefly at Sitka, old Russian capital on Sitka Sound, almost in the shadow of Mount Edgecumbe, and then heads east and south over the divide of Baranof Island. Baranof is a little higher and a little more exposed than most of the islands of the Alexander Archipelago, and it still supports a small ice cap that feeds short valley glaciers. Once over the divide, the plane drops rapidly into a glacial valley and flies only a few hundred feet above Red Bluff Bay where there is a small mass of red igneous rock containing a little chromite.

As the plane leaves the shore of Baranof Island and passes over Chatham Strait, there is a fine view eastward over Frederick Sound and beyond, to the glittering icy peaks of the main Coast Range on the distant horizon. From this vantage point it is easy to imagine the stupendous sheets of ice that poured through this broad channel during the Pleistocene period, overriding even the high divide of Baranof Island.

Again the plane changes course and heads almost due north on a beeline for Juneau. As it flies over the southern end of Admiralty Island, one sees above the timbered lower slopes of the mountains the flat and gently dipping lava flows of Tertiary age that lie in a structural trough cut off by the great fault under Chatham Strait, only a short distance to the west. Soon the plane reaches Kootznahoo Inlet, where attempts have been made to mine coal interbedded with Tertiary volcanic rocks.

A few more miles and the plane passes over beautiful Hasselborg Lake. If the glacier that gouged its basin had cut a little deeper or if sea level had risen a little higher, this would have been another arm of the sea.

Within minutes the plane crosses Stephens Passage and descends in a long slope as it courses along Gastineau Channel, the walls of which are scored horizontally by ice abrasion. Finally, the plane lands on the smooth water of Juneau harbor and taxis to a landing at the airline float.

DON J. MILLER

Gulf of Alaska Area

The Gulf of Alaska area is an arcuate, predominantly mountainous belt, 800 miles long and 20 to 110 miles wide, bordering the Gulf of Alaska from Kodiak Island on the west to Cross Sound on the east, including the Kodiak, the Kenai, and the Chugach Mountains and the Alaskan part of the St. Elias Mountains (pl. 1). It is part of the Pacific mountain system, separated from the more northerly branch by Shelikof Strait, Cook Inlet, and the belt formed by the Kenai lowland, the Matanuska and Chitina valleys, and the Copper River plateau. The St. Elias Mountains, shared by Alaska and Canada, form a distinct physiographic province set off by rather arbitrary boundaries from the Coast Range on the southeast and from the Chugach and the Wrangell Mountains and the Alaska Range on the northwest. Most of the Alaskan part of the St. Elias Mountains, however, is topographically continuous with, and in many respects is geologically similar to, the Chugach Mountains.

Furthermore, the St. Elias and Chugach-Kenai provinces share a third distinctive physiographic subdivision, the coastal lowland and foothill belt extending from the Copper River southeastward to Icy Point. Glaciers are an equally striking and prominent feature of the St. Elias Mountains, the Chugach-Kenai Mountains, and the coastal lowland and foothill subprovince. It is fitting, therefore, to describe the area bordering the Gulf of Alaska as a unit, and point out differences between the surface features and geologic environment of its three physiographic subdivisions.

The following description of the Gulf of Alaska area may be likened to the architectural study of a building. We examine first the mountains, plains, valleys, and other surface features—the external form of the building. Next we examine the rocks—the building materials; then the geologic processes that formed and shaped the rocks—the methods and history of construction; and finally, we study the influence of the geologic environment and surface features on other natural features—the environment created by the building.

The southeastern Alaska "panhandle" is joined to the "pan" by the highest coastal mountains in the world—the St. Elias Mountains. Roughly, half of the St. Elias province lies in Canada. Between Mount St. Elias and Mount Fairweather the international boundary follows the crest of the chain at an average distance of only 30 miles from the coast. In that stretch, the boundary turns on such impressive natural markers as Mount St. Elias (18,008 feet), Mount Vancouver (15,700 feet), Mount Fairweather (15,-300 feet), and Mount Hubbard (14,950 feet). Within the St. Elias Mountains are located the second and fourth highest peaks on the North American continent (Mount Logan, 19,850 feet, and Mount St. Elias), as well as twelve other peaks that exceed in altitude the highest in the continental United States.

The St. Elias Mountains are about 300 miles long, and have a maximum width of about 100 miles, excluding the coastal plain and foothill belt. Near the Alaska-Yukon border, the mountains merge with the Chugach and the Wrangell Mountains and with the Nutzotin Mountains of the Alaska Range. The Fairweather Range, which forms the southeastern narrowest part of the St. Elias province, is higher and topographically distinct from the adjacent Coast Range.

I. C. Russell, leader of an expedition attempting to climb Mount St. Elias in 1891, gained a divide on the crest of the range at an altitude of 14,500 feet, and from that vantage point viewed for the first time the then unknown area to the north. Russell's impression of the scene is an eloquent description of the St. Elias Mountains:

> I expected to see a comparatively low, forested country, stretching away to the north, with lakes and rivers and perhaps some signs of human habitation. What met my astonished

gaze was a vast snow-covered region, limitless in expanse, through which hundreds, perhaps thousands, of bare, angular mountain peaks projected. There was not a stream, not a lake, and not a vestige of vegetation of any kind in sight. A more desolate or utterly lifeless land one never beheld. Vast, smooth snow surfaces without crevasses stretched away to limitless distances, broken only by jagged and angular mountain peaks.

So the St. Elias Mountains remain today—desolate, icebound, uninhabited except for a few small settlements around the fringe—still a challenge to the explorer and mountaineer, a vast field laboratory for the student of glaciers.

So rugged and difficult of access are the St. Elias Mountains that little is known of their geology. Reconnaissance investigations in the Fairweather Range, around Yakutat Bay, and in the northwestern part, together with information gained by climbing expeditions, indicate that the mountains consist mainly of bedded sedimentary and volcanic rocks of Paleozoic and Mesozoic age. These rocks have been intensely disturbed by folding and faulting, and have been altered by deep burial and by heat and mineralizing solutions emanating from bodies of intrusive igneous rock such as now form many of the high peaks.

The St. Elias Mountains owe their ruggedness and great height in large part to uplift along northwest-trending faults. Many of these faults are revealed by the topography. Some of them are marked by elongated troughs developed in shattered, and hence more easily eroded, rocks; others are marked by steep scarps on the uplifted sides, like the abrupt seaward face of the St. Elias Mountains between Icy Bay and Icy Point. Between Lituya Bay and Dry Bay, the trough along the fault at the base of the scarp is largely filled with ice. Farther west the same fault zone, if not the same fault, lies along the northwest-trending part of Disenchantment Bay, and at the base of the steep south-facing scarp that includes Mount Cook, Mount Augusta, and Mount St. Elias. Another great arcuate fault system bounds the St. Elias Mountains on the northeast, continuing southward into the Lynn Canal–Chatham Strait trough and northwestward into the Alaska Range. This is described in the sections dealing with southeastern Alaska and the Alaska Range.

The Chugach and the Kenai Mountains comprise the 450-mile central segment of the mountain chain bordering the Gulf of Alaska. They extend from the St. Elias Mountains on the east to the southwest end of the Kenai

Peninsula and vary in width from 30 to 110 miles. East of a line extending northwestward from the mouth of the Copper River, the Chugach Mountains trend slightly north of west, rising to an average maximum altitude of 7,000 to 8,000 feet. The three highest peaks in this part of the range, Mount Miller (11,000 feet), Mount Steller (10,267 feet), and Mount Tom White (9,000 feet), rise along the southern front overlooking the coastal lowland and foothill belt. The Chugach Mountains to the west swing sharply southwestward, their southeastern part being partly submerged beneath Prince William Sound. Near this sharp bend rise the highest peaks of the Chugach Mountains, Mount Marcus Baker (13,176 feet) and Mount Witherspoon (12,023 feet).

The Kenai Mountains are geologically and topographically a continuation of the Chugach Mountains, from which they are separated by the low transverse trough formed by Turnagain Arm and Passage Canal. That depression is the route of the Whittier-Potter segment of the Alaska Railroad. The Kenai Mountains rise to an average altitude of 3,000 to 5,000 feet; the highest peak, unnamed, has an altitude of 6,800 feet.

The Chugach and the Kenai Mountains are extremely rugged, the average relief of their valley walls being 5,000 feet or more. Powerful glaciers have converted an older system of V-shaped stream valleys into a rugged, deeply indented coast and U-shaped valleys. And because the glaciers and streams follow two directions of weakness in the bedrocks, one parallel and the other normal to the axis of the mountain chain, a rectangular pattern of ridges and valleys has developed, especially in the country bordering the Copper River and near the Alaska Railroad between Seward and Portage.

The St. Elias, the Chugach, and the Kenai Mountains include the most extensive system of valley glaciers and some of the largest ice fields of North America. The mountains adjoin a region of heavy precipitation, and at high altitudes much of this falls as snow which slowly accumulates and changes through compaction and alternate freezing and thawing into fields of ice. From centers of accumulation, such as the Harding Ice Field in the Kenai Mountains, the ice field about Mount Witherspoon in the western Chugach Mountains, and the Bagley Ice Field in the eastern Chugach Mountains, glaciers flow slowly down the valleys. On the coastal side of the mountains, most of the larger glaciers descend below 500 feet, and many reach tidewater. The head of Yakutat Bay and the northern and western shores of Prince William Sound are especially noteworthy for the number and size of tidal glacier fronts. On the interior flank of the mountain chain most of the larger glaciers end at altitudes between 1,500 and 3,000 feet.

Because the glaciers are long, most of the rivers in the Gulf of Alaska area are short. They are muddy and swift during the summer, but during the winter they are greatly reduced in volume. The Copper River, one of the major drainage systems in Alaska, drains from the plateau of that name into the Gulf of Alaska by way of a steep-walled valley across the Chugach Mountains. In its lower course, it divides into many channels on a broad delta, filling an embayment that once extended far into the Chugach Mountains. The Copper River is the route followed by the now abandoned Copper River and Northwestern Railroad, over which the rich ore from the Kennicott copper mines was hauled to the seaport of Cordova; it is also the route proposed for a highway that will again link Cordova with interior Alaska.

The Alsek River, which is similar in many respects to the Copper River, has cut a low-altitude valley from interior Canada through the heart of the St. Elias Mountains to the coast at Dry Bay. Part of the interior flank of the St. Elias Mountains, including a small area in Alaska, drains 1,300 miles to the Bering Sea by way of the Yukon River system.

The predominantly mountainous cluster of islands, of which Kodiak Island is the largest, is topographically, geologically, and structurally a continuation of the Chugach-Kenai mountain chain. The Kodiak Mountains rise to an average altitude of 2,000 to 4,000 feet. During the time of maximum glaciation they were almost completely covered by ice, so that many preëxisting stream valleys were scoured below sea level and only the highest peaks and ridges escaped glacial sculpture. As the ice retreated and sea level rose, the deepened valleys were flooded, the shore line was embayed, and the tops of some of the ridges were left as islands. Glaciation also accounts for the almost complete absence of Sitka spruce from the southern two-thirds of the island group. After deglaciation, the spruce forest was reëstablished first in the northern part, and its front has moved southward an appreciable distance during historic time.

The arcuate form of the Chugach-Kenai-Kodiak mountain chain is closely paralleled by the structural trends and the outcrop patterns of the underlying bedrocks. A thick series of bedded, slightly to moderately metamorphosed sedimentary and volcanic rocks of Mesozoic and late Paleozoic age predominates. The most abundant rocks are slate, argillite, graywacke, and greenstone, all characteristically of somber color. These layered rocks are complexly crumpled; in many places they stand vertically or nearly so, and they are cut by many faults. Masses of granitic rock, some of considerable size, intrude the layered deposits. These features are clearly revealed in steep valley walls, tunnels, and cuts along the Alaska Railroad between Whittier and Potter, along the Richardson Highway between Valdez and Tonsina, and along the abandoned Copper River and Northwestern Railroad between Chitina and the coast.

Movement along large faults roughly parallel to the trend of the mountain chain as been a major factor in the development of the present form and high relief of the Chugach, the Kenai, and the Kodiak Mountains. The fault along the seaward front of the St. Elias Mountains near Yakutat Bay continues westward along the southern front of the eastern Chugach Mountains at least as far as the Copper River. Two major northeast-trending faults are present in the Kodiak Mountains. The abrupt rise of the northwestern and northern flanks of the Kenai and the Chugach Mountains from the adjacent lowland suggests faulting; so does the presence within the mountains of long, relatively straight trenches such as the one occupied by the Bagley Ice Field.

Around most of the Gulf of Alaska, the mountains rise directly from the shore, the coast is extremely irregular, and the water is deep close to shore. Between the delta of the Copper River and Icy Point, on the contrary, the coast line is remarkably even, the water is relatively shallow for a considerable distance offshore, and a lowland and foothill belt, 2 to 40 miles wide, lies between the sea and the main front of the Chugach and the St. Elias Mountains. In the 250-mile stretch between Cape St. Elias and Icy Point there are no offshore islands and only three bays. A plain of low relief borders the shore. Beyond this plain rise the so-called foothills— actually rugged mountains 2,000 to 6,000 feet high—yet "hills" compared to the still higher front of the Chugach and the St. Elias Mountains.

The differences between the coastal lowland and foothill belt and the rest of the area bordering the Gulf of Alaska are especially apparent to anyone who dares to take a small boat across the stormy Gulf between the sheltered waters of southeastern Alaska and Prince William Sound. If he places his charts beside a geologic map he will see that the stretch of regular, inhospitable coast line and the bordering lowlands and foothills, coincides closely with a belt of sedimentary rocks of Tertiary age. Major faults account for the scarplike seaward front of the Chugach and the St. Elias Mountains between the Copper River and Yakutat Bay, also from Icy Point northwestward to the vicinity of Cape Fairweather. The extensive lowlands are underlain by Quaternary sediments—sand, gravel, and mud deposited by the sea, streams, and glaciers on a sea- and stream-planed surface of Tertiary and older bedrocks.

The Tertiary deposits in the foothills include coal-bearing rocks, laid down in part on land, overlain by predominantly marine sediments in which occur most of the oil and gas seepages of the Katalla and Yakataga districts. Over most of the lowland and foothill belt these Tertiary rocks are complexly deformed and are broken by many faults. In the Robinson Mountains of the Yakataga district, the complex structure is strikingly revealed by bare, nearly vertical cliffs carved in contrastingly colored layers.

Glaciers confined in valleys in the Chugach and the St. Elias Mountains and in the bordering foothills debouch on to the coastal plain to form broad lobes called piedmont glaciers. The largest of these, the Malaspina Glacier, is so vast as to cover most of the coastal plain between Yakutat Bay and Icy Bay, an area about equal in size to that of the State of Rhode Island. Seismic measurements indicate that near the center this ice sheet is as much as 2,000 feet thick. Bering Glacier, including its piedmont lobe and the 10-mile-wide feeder that extends across the foothill belt, is about equal in area to the Malaspina Glacier. Guyot Glacier, a large ice field lying entirely within the foothill belt, discharges into Icy Bay along an ice-cliff front 3 miles long and 100 to 200 feet high. La Perouse Glacier, a smaller piedmont glacier near the southeastern end of the coastal lowland and foothill belt, is the only glacier in Alaska that discharges directly into the open ocean.

The area bordering the Gulf of Alaska was the object of some of the earliest geologic studies made in Alaska, and although it has continued to receive a fair share of attention, its geologic history is still very imperfectly known. The reason is easy to understand: in the more remote parts of the St. Elias Mountains and eastern Chugach Mountains, large areas remain unexplored and virtually unknown except through aerial reconnaissance and aerial photography. Even in the more accessible parts of the mountain chain, where glacier-bared rock walls of valley and fiord and thousands of miles of bedrock shore line afford ideal conditions for deciphering the geology, detailed studies have left many problems unsolved. There are three chief difficulties confronting the geologist: (1) complex deformation of the rocks, involving development of cleavage and shear planes, and endless repetition or even inversion of the normal sequence through folding and faulting; (2) prevalence of monotonous sequences of volcanic and clastic rocks many thousands of feet in thickness but lacking units distinctive enough to be traced over long distances; and (3) lack or scarcity of fossils to provide clues to the chronological sequence.

The oldest rocks of the Chugach–St. Elias mountain chain are of Paleozoic age, and are preserved in a belt on the northern flank, between the meridian 146° West and the Canadian border. They consist of slates, schists, and altered limestones interbedded with subordinate layers of volcanic materials and overlain by a thick series of lava flows and explosive ejecta, now altered to greenstones. Shells and other hard parts of marine animals indicate that these Paleozoic rocks were laid down during the Mississippian and Permian periods.

Southern Alaska was again occupied by seas and by submarine and island volcanoes during late Triassic and early Jurassic times. Rocks recording this chapter in the history of the Gulf of Alaska area form a narrow belt along the western and northwestern flanks of the mountain chain from the Kodiak group of islands to the southwestern margin of the Copper River plateau. They are well exposed near Seldovia, where they contain marine fossils, and along the Alaska Railroad on the north shore of Turnagain Arm between Potter and a point about 2 miles east of Rainbow. Volcanic and sedimentary deposits, perhaps of the same age, partly altered to schists and other metamorphic rocks, are present along the seaward front of the St. Elias Mountains, and near Cordova, as well as on several islands in Prince William Sound.

From middle Jurassic time intermittently throughout the remainder of the Mesozoic era, that is, from about 60 million to 140 million years ago, the area now occupied by southern Alaska was affected by powerful earth movements that produced fold-belts arranged concentrically about the present Gulf of Alaska. The depressed or negative belts became troughs that sank as sediments accumulated within them, while the upheaved or positive belts rose and thus became subject to erosion. These important crustal disturbances were accompanied by, and were partly the result of, intrusions of granitic rocks.

During late Cretaceous time, or possibly still earlier in the Mesozoic era, the sea invaded a trough approximately on the present site of the Chugach-Kenai-Kodiak mountain chain, and mud and muddy sand were deposited in alternating layers to a total thickness of many thousands of feet. These deposits, compacted and hardened by deep burial and subjected to deformation and uplift during one or more periods of mountain building, now comprise the dark-colored slates and graywackes that make up a major part of the mountain chain.

The rocks near the town of Kodiak, along both the Seward and Whittier branches of the Alaska Railroad to a point 2 miles east of Rainbow, and along the Richardson Highway between Valdez and Ernestine are representative of this sequence. Careful search for fossils along an outcrop belt 500 miles in length has resulted in the discovery of only a few diagnostic fossils, all representing a single genus of oysterlike clam. Either the arm of the sea in which the muddy sediments were laid down was almost barren of marine organisms with hard parts, or conditions were such that the shells were destroyed before burial.

The Mesozoic events described in the preceding paragraphs laid the basic framework for the present arrangement of mountains, lowlands, rock units, major faults, and structural trends in concentric arcs about the Gulf of Alaska. During a second major period of mountain building, at the close of the Mesozoic era or in early Tertiary time, a mountain chain approximating the present shape and trend of the St. Elias, the Chugach, the Kenai, and the Kodiak Mountains emerged from the sea. These ancestral mountains probably were worn down to a low level in Tertiary time. Evidence of at least one ancient erosion surface is found in the accordant summit levels of the peaks in the eastern Chugach Mountains, and in the anomalous course of the Alsek River across the heart of the St. Elias Mountains.

While the early Tertiary mountains were being lowered by erosion, sediments, including beds of coal, were being deposited above sea level in the present area of the coastal lowland and foothill belt. The climate at this time was mild, not only in the coastal area but farther north in Alaska, as indicated by the presence in the coal-bearing strata of fossil leaves of warm temperate and subtropical species of plants and trees. During late Eocene time the sea again invaded the continental margin, and marine deposits continued to accumulate there into late Tertiary time, possibly into the Pleistocene. Shells of marine organisms found in sediments of late Eocene to earliest Miocene age indicate subtropical to warm temperate water, but most fossil shells in the younger Tertiary marine sediments are identical with or similar to shells of marine animals now living in the cool water of the Gulf of Alaska. Late Tertiary marine sediments in the Yakataga district and in the vicinity of Lituya Bay contain much ice-rafted material, proof that there were glaciers in the bordering mountains long before the climax of continental glaciation in the North American continent, just as they have persisted in the Gulf of Alaska area long after the climax.

During late Tertiary or Pleistocene time, uplift of the St. Elias-Chugach-Kenai-Kodiak mountain chain was renewed, and the bordering belt of Tertiary sediments was folded, faulted, and probably elevated above the sea. Wave-cut terraces along the coast at numerous levels up to a height of 1,600 feet or more show that the upward movement of the land relative to the sea was intermittent. The characteristic steplike topography of the elevated terraces and adjacent wave-cut cliffs is especially conspicuous between Icy Point and Cape Fairweather, and on Middleton Island far out in the Gulf of Alaska. Frequent earthquakes in the area indicate that the mountain-building movements still continue. In September, 1899, displacement along one or more faults near Yakutat Bay caused earthquake shocks that were recorded around the world. During the most violent of these shocks, part of the shore of Yakutat Bay suddenly rose a maximum distance of 47 feet. Parts of the former beach line, marked by a wave-cut notch in the bedrock and by barnacles attached to rocks, may still be seen in the inner part of the bay.

Deposition of sediments by rivers, glaciers, and the sea has played, and is continuing to play, a major part in forming extensive lowlands such as the Copper River delta and the coastal plains marginal to the Bering and Malaspina glaciers. How embayments between bedrock headlands are being filled with sediments is well illustrated by Controller Bay. There Okalee Spit and Kanak Island, a sand bar and sand island built by the westward set of the current combined with the prevailing southeasterly storm waves, nearly close off the embayment between the bedrock headlands of Cape Suckling and Point Hey. The sheltered bay thus formed is being rapidly filled by sediment carried in by the Bering River and other streams draining from the Bering Glacier.

When the Pleistocene glaciers were largest, the Gulf of Alaska area probably was covered by a continuous ice cap above which projected only the highest peaks and ridges. The effects of this glaciation are recorded largely in deep fiords, U-shaped valleys, and other surface forms of glacial erosion, rather than in glacial deposits, for the glaciers left most of their load outside the area. To the south, the glaciers extended beyond the present coast and possibly coalesced to form an ice shelf extending well out in the Gulf of Alaska. Broad submarine troughs on the submerged shelf between the Kodiak Mountains and the Kenai Mountains, at the entrance to Prince William Sound between Hinchinbrook and Montague islands, and off Yakutat Bay are believed to have been formed by glacial scour.

Two or more periods of moderate readvance of the glaciers in the Gulf of Alaska area in geologically recent time are recorded in glacial deposits and forms of glacial erosion, in the vegetation, and even in historical records. The constricted entrance to Lituya Bay and the crescentic shoals at the mouth of Yakutat Bay and of Icy Bay are due to end moraines that record a recent maximum stand of the glaciers tributary to these bays. Maps and eye-witness accounts show that an ice sheet formed between 1886 and 1902, by Guyot and Malaspina glaciers, completely filled the present Icy Bay, projecting into the ocean as Icy Cape. By 1953, the tidal front of Guyot Glacier had retreated about 18 miles and the margin of Malaspina Glacier stood 2 miles or more back from the shore of Icy Bay. In 1794, according to the explorer Vancouver, the ice front was not more than 5 or 6 miles back from the entrance. Still earlier, judging from the legends of the Yakutat natives, Icy Bay may have been much as it is today.

The ice lobe that occupied Lituya Bay not more than a few centuries ago can be reconstructed with considerable accuracy from the terminal moraine on the terraced coastal plain and the lateral moraines extending into the mountains along both sides of the bay. The ice surface, where it emerged from the mountains 3 miles from the coast, stood about 1,200 feet above the present sea level. This advance occurred before 1786, when the French explorer La Perouse found the shores of the bay forested and the glacier fronts a little farther back than at present, but probably not more than two hundred years earlier. The forest growing within the terminal moraine is noticeably less mature than the one outside.

This brief discussion of the geologic history of the Gulf of Alaska area may properly be closed with the reminder that the events just described involve a time span of perhaps 250 million years. There are many millions of years for which no record has been preserved, and perhaps other periods the record of which the geologist has failed to recognize. Most of the changes, such as the uplift of mountains and invasion of the land by the sea, took place very slowly, indeed at an almost imperceptible rate; on the contrary, some changes have been recorded in historical times, and others, for example the elevation of the beaches at Yakutat Bay, have been almost instantaneous.

The Gulf of Alaska area is one of bold contrasts: within a short distance, the traveler may experience many extremes of environment characteristic of the farthest limits of the territory; forest and underbrush as dense as any in the southernmost part of Alaska, adjoining vast ice-covered lands as desolate and more arctic in appearance than northern Alaska; the fog, heavy rainfall, dense clouds, violent storms, and uniform temperature of the Aleutians; the aridity and extremes of summer and winter temperature characteristic of the upper Yukon Valley. Mount St. Elias, rivaling Mount McKinley in height, towers over a coastal plain that, in part, is as flat and swampy as the Yukon-Kuskokwim delta; railway, highway, and airline routes connect thriving seaports with interior and southeastern Alaska, yet within the area lie thousands of square miles of wilderness counted among the least known and least frequented parts of Alaska.

ROBERT F. BLACK

Wrangell Mountains

The Wrangell Mountains, sometimes called the "jewels" of central Alaska, are a compact cluster of volcanic mountains resting on a basement of metamorphosed and mineralized sedimentary and igneous rocks. They lie in the southeastern part of the main body of Alaska, between the Alaska Range to the north and the Chugach Mountains to the south. Rising as they do more than 10,000 feet above the Copper River plateau, they must be counted among the most beautiful of mountains. Over a dozen peaks rise more than 12,000 feet above sea level in an area measuring about 100 by 70 miles across. Few have climbed the Wrangell Mountains, although on Mount Wrangell itself, which rises to a height of 14,006 feet, there is now a research project supported by the Office of Naval Research. Spectacular distant views of the mountains may be had from vantage points such as Copper Center, Gakona, and Chistochina on roads that skirt the region on three sides, but only the traveler who equips himself properly and goes by pack train deep into the interior can appreciate fully the majesty and wildness of these mountains.

Prospectors, miners, and businessmen came to the Territory in large numbers following discovery of the Klondike gold deposits in 1896. By 1898, much of the immigration was directed toward the drainage area of the Copper River, on the northern, southern, and western sides of the Wrangell

Mountains. The newcomers, seeing native copper implements in wide use among the Indians, searched intensively for the metal and were soon rewarded by discovery of many ore bodies, among them those that developed into some of the richest copper mines in the world, namely, the Kennicott mines. From the time of the early Russian explorers until the Kennicott mines were closed in 1938, the Copper River basin, the Chitina River area, and the Wrangell Mountains were the scene of extensive mineral exploration. Now, encouraged by the development of additional copper showings, by cosmic-ray research on top of Mount Wrangell, and by improved transportation, interest in the region is again awakening.

The geographic and geologic explorations begun by Henry T. Allen in 1885, and continued by Frederick Schwatka and Charles W. Hayes in 1891, Frank C. Schrader in 1898, Oscar Rohn in 1899, and Fred H. Moffit, are among the epics of the Territory. Nevertheless, the geology of the Wrangell Mountains is only partly known. Rugged ridges and peaks dissected by glacial valleys thwart all but the most ambitious and hardy, and mapping is laborious and slow; indeed, many of the inner heights have yet to feel the footsteps of the geologist.

The higher parts of the Wrangell Mountains and many of the adjacent foothills are carved in lava flows and fragmental volcanic materials, mainly andesitic and basaltic in composition, that were spread over a preëxisting surface of strong relief. These volcanic rocks are spoken of as the "Wrangell lavas." The eruptions that produced them began in Tertiary time, perhaps 50 million years ago, and have continued intermittently ever since. Mount Wrangell erupted within the last century, and even now clouds of steam and ash are occasionally to be seen rising from the summit crater. Mount Drum is a much older volcano, for it has been deeply dissected by erosion and its steep ridges terminate in a sharp peak. Other volcanoes, such as Mount Sanford and Mount Blackburn, are of intermediate age (see pl. 8).

The products of these volcanoes are largely buried beneath perennial snow and ice, but in many places they form precipitous cliffs with contrasting colors that result primarily from alteration of the rocks by weathering and volcanic emanations. Many lavas contain gas-formed bubbles or vesicles, some of which are filled with light-colored varieties of quartz. Some flows contain large crystals of amber-colored feldspar in a fine-grained groundmass; other flows, fragments of which are present in the moraine on the west side of Frederika Glacier, are black, glassy obsidians. Indeed, many of the volcanic rocks closely resemble those to be seen in Yellowstone National Park and in Hawaii.

Local accumulations of conglomerate, variegated clays, and coaly material are present between the volcanic layers. On the east side of Frederika Valley, for instance, there are beautifully tinted fresh-water sediments that contain well-preserved leaves. Where horizontal sheets of massive lava alternate with these softer layers of sediment or with beds of ash, erosion produces flat-topped hills, precipitous cliffs, and steplike terraces such as are well displayed in the upper part of Chimney Mountain, on the west side of the Nizina Glacier.

Beneath the rocks just described are much older ones, some of which form conspicuous cliffs and contain copper and other metallic minerals of economic value. The oldest of these basement rocks are altered submarine lavas, ashes, muds, and limy sediments laid down in Mississippian time, approximately 250 million years ago. They are widespread on the northern side of the Chitina Valley, and in many places are cut by granular igneous intrusive rocks of various kinds.

On top of the Mississippian rocks lies a thick pile of Permian lavas and tuffs interbedded with fossiliferous limestones and a little slate. Then follows a great accumulation of lava flows, perhaps 160 to 200 million years old, resembling the youngest volcanic rocks of the region except that they are extremely altered. These flows, the Nikolai greenstones, lie along the north side of the Chitina Valley; they contain many copper prospects and are famous as the source of abundant nuggets of native copper.

After all the foregoing rocks had been folded and uplifted above sea level to form mountains, and after these in their turn had been completely erased by erosion, limestones and shales of late Triassic age were deposited in seas that covered the site of the Wrangell Mountains about 150 million years ago. These sedimentary rocks aggregate about 5,000 feet in thickness and are almost entirely exposed between McCarthy Creek and the Chitistone River (see pl. 10). The massive limestones form tremendous, bare cliffs, and are famous as the host rocks of the rich Kennicott copper ores. The thinner-bedded Triassic rocks are characterized by conspicuous folding and faulting, and by the presence of black chert nodules among the limestones.

All of the rocks of the Wrangell Mountains are cut by igneous intrusions, some of which consist of dark, coarse-grained materials, though the most conspicuous and widespread are dikes and sills of light-colored granite.

Gold is less important than copper in the Wrangell Mountains, but it is mined from placers in stream valleys within the foothills, especially in the Nizina and Chisana areas. Gold and silver are also present in widely scattered veins among the bedrocks, but they are seldom seen, and some large igneous bodies contain copper, silver, gold, molybdenum, zinc, and other metals.

Outstanding in the later geologic history of the region is the glaciation that began after most of the Wrangell lavas had been erupted. One of the longest valley glaciers of Alaska originates on the east side of Mount Wrangell, terminating at Nabesna, about 60 miles away, where its meltwaters form the Nabesna River, a major tributary of the Tanana. The present glaciers and the ice cap of Mount Wrangell are, however, merely remnants of enormous ice sheets that buried the surrounding lowlands to depths of several thousands of feet during the Pleistocene period. Fragments of Wrangell lava were then carried by ice as far as the southern part of the Alaska Range and the northern part of the Chugach Mountains. Unfortunately, the former road from Strelna to the Kuskulana Glacier and the railroad from Chitina to Kennicott are no longer accessible to the tourist; only mountaineering parties may reach the inner, higher reaches of the glaciated areas where superb scenery is to be seen in all directions.

ROBERT F. BLACK

Copper River Plateau

The Copper River plateau, directly west of the Wrangell Mountains, is often referred to as the Copper River basin, and its lowest part is traversed by the central stretch of the Copper River. The Richardson Highway from Tonsina to Paxson divides the plateau from south to north; the Glenn Highway, on its way to Anchorage, extends westward through the southern part for about 60 miles from the Richardson Highway. The Edgerton Cutoff to Chitina and part of the Glenn Highway northeast from Gulkana toward Tok Junction add another 100 miles of relatively easily traveled road, and new highways from Paxson to Cantwell and Mount McKinley National Park across the northern part of the area are under construction. These roads provide inspiring views of the mountains that rim the basin—the Alaska Range to the north, the Talkeetna Mountains to the west, the Chugach Mountains to the south, and the Wrangell Mountains to the east.

The scenery close at hand seems unspectacular compared with the distant views, yet it arouses a number of questions in the mind of the inquiring observer. Why is there so much gravel? What caused the flat and rolling terrain dotted with ponds and lakes? Why, with so much gravel, does water stand on the surface in so many places? What makes so many trees tilt into shallow ponds and lakes where wave action cannot be strong? The answers to these and similar questions lie in the physiographic development of the plateau during the last few million years.

Almost all of the surficial deposits were laid down during Quaternary time. Isolated low hills and ridges in the northern part of the plateau consist of metamorphosed rocks of Paleozoic age, greenstones, schists, limestones, and basic and dioritic intrusive rocks. Gneisses and schists of this age are exposed in cuts along the Richardson Highway north of Meier's Roadhouse, but generally these ancient rocks are overlooked because they do not form prominent features.

Other gneisses and schists, including minor amounts of tuff, fine-grained basalt, shale, and thin-bedded chert of Mississippian and Pennsylvanian age are to be seen along the eastern part of the highway into Chitina where it passes through a narrow gorge. Along the Glenn Highway, west of Eureka, poorly consolidated, fossiliferous sandstone and sandy shale of Cretaceous age are to be seen in low hills largely buried by gravel, and the landslide at "Mud Mountain" (mile 142), is in these rocks. Elsewhere, gravel of Quaternary age blankets all but a few isolated hills and ridges of older rocks.

It is not surprising, from what has been said, that it is difficult to reconstruct the early history of the Copper River plateau. Yet even the meager record suffices to show that about 200 million years ago the area was inundated by shallow, shifting seas in which limy, sandy, and muddy sediments accumulated while lavas and ashes were being discharged by submarine and island volcanoes.

During the next 150 million years the bordering regions were occupied from time to time by fluctuating seas and volcanoes, and they were subjected both to mountain building and erosion, but the record of those times within the plateau itself is meager. Seas were finally driven from the region during the Tertiary period, perhaps 50 million years ago, when it was again uplifted. It was then that the major mountains and lowlands were blocked out by crustal deformation. Differential uplift of the surrounding mountains or downfaulting of the plateau seems to have produced the initial basin form, but the full story has still to be deciphered.

During the last million years, that is, during Pleistocene time, the climate grew colder and glaciation became the dominant geologic process. First the high mountains formed gathering places for snow and ice; then the glaciers slowly moved to lower elevations, coalescing into aprons along the fronts of the ranges until gradually the entire basin was filled with ice. Exactly how thick the ice was cannot be told; the thickness must have varied from place to place and from time to time, but locally it must have been several thousands of feet. Unmistakable signs of the former extent of the ice are to be seen in the mantle of glacial debris thickly scattered over the lowlands, in the abandonment of old drainage lines, and in the initiation of new ones.

Ice spread into the lowlands more than once, for here, as elsewhere in Alaska, minor climatic changes caused glaciers to advance and retreat many times. Indeed there were intervals when the climate may have been as warm or even warmer than it is today so that glaciers vanished entirely from the Copper River plateau.

The traveler will have no difficulty in imagining how the gravel, sand, and silt deposits were laid down by the glaciers as they waxed and waned. Unsorted and unstratified deposits were formed directly by the ice while well-sorted and stratified deposits were laid down by streams or in lakes and ponds fed by meltwaters, just as similar ones are being produced today. Along the Copper, Susitna, Tazlina, and Klutina rivers in particular, the deposits are more than 500 feet thick, but toward the sides of the basin they become thinner and finally disappear.

Once the newly deposited materials were exposed in the bars of glacial streams, the finer particles were picked up by winds and carried away. That is why one now sees actively growing sand dunes along most of the major streams and finer silt deposits farther from their source.

Some low mounds within the plateau were also formed by wind action, but most of them are glacial moraines. The debris of which they are composed is particularly impervious to surface water; hence, ponds and lakes develop in the depressions. Some of these depressions are completely filled with vegetation, but most are only a few thousand years old and are only filled in part.

Other lakes result from the permafrost that formed after the departure of the glacial ice. Permafrost, or perennially frozen ground, refers to a zone of surficial material or bedrock at a variable depth beneath the surface in which temperatures below freezing have persisted continuously for a long time, generally from two to tens of thousands of years. In ground of this kind, ice surrounds the rock particles and often fills the pores; hence surface water, unable to penetrate into the normal ground water zone, accumulates to form bogs and lakes. Where vegetation overlying permafrost has been stripped by fires or by man, the ground is exposed to more intense solar heating so that the ground ice melts, causing the surface to settle or cave. In this way, thermokarst landforms develop, the most readily apparent features of which are cave-in lakes.

Advances of ice over the lowland produced major changes in the drainage of the Copper River plateau. Drainage was formerly northward via the Mentasta Valley, and the Copper River at Chitina, as we know it now, did not exist. As the glaciers partly filled the basin, the Mentasta outlet became blocked by ice and runoff waters overflowed the rocky barriers south of Chitina, where Wood Canyon is now located; and because the glaciers remained static long enough, their first random runoff waters developed gradually into a side glacial stream which through the years cut the narrow, deep, rock-walled canyon now followed by the highway south to Chitina, leaving several lakes in the deeper portions. The small lake at Chitina is another of these glacier-formed lakes, now abandoned high above the present drainage to the east. Wood and other canyons along the Lower Copper River were also cut during this same period. The Copper River itself cut down its floor so rapidly that the less powerful tributary streams were unable to keep pace; hence falls, such as Liberty Falls north of Chitina, developed where the tributaries tumbled into the main river.

On top of the ridge separating the old channel of the Copper River from its present course there are peat deposits beneath a protective cover of wind-blown sand. These deposits accumulated on the bottoms of lakes that were present before the relocation and downcutting of the Copper River.

Since glacial time, uplift of the area, coupled with increase in runoff as a result of slight warming, has increased the erosive power of the major streams so that they have incised their channels into the glacial fill of the Copper River plateau. Numerous fresh slumps and landslides along the steeper parts of many valleys show that erosion is still going on at a rapid rate.

Mineral deposits are uncommon in the Copper River plateau, except for scattered deposits of placer gold. Most placer deposits are destroyed by advancing glaciers, and not enough time has elapsed since the glaciers retreated to permit concentration of economic quantities of heavy minerals.

FARRELL F. BARNES

Talkeetna Mountains

Two of the most majestic mountain ranges of Alaska encircle the north shore of the Gulf of Alaska in concentric arcs, namely, the glacier-clad Kenai-Chugach Range, which follows the coast, and the towering Alaska Range, which lies farther inland. Between the two, barely separated from the Alaska Range to the north by the broad headwater valley of the Nenana River and from the Chugach Range on the south by the Matanuska Valley, lies a rugged mountainous area, roughly 100 miles from north to south and 70 miles from east to west, known as the Talkeetna Mountains. No roads cross this relatively unknown area, much of which has yet to be mapped geologically, but it is completely encircled by major transportation lines. To the west the Alaska Railroad follows the Susitna River Valley; to the south the Glenn Highway follows the bordering Matanuska Valley; to the east—although separated from the mountains by the broad Copper River plateau—passes the Richardson Highway; and to the north, connecting the Richardson Highway and the railroad, lies the recently opened Denali Highway.

A geologic picture of the Talkeetna Mountains can best be given by a brief review of their history. The early records are obscure, for many pages are missing. Rocks deposited during the long pre-Paleozoic and Paleozoic

38

eras are exposed only in a few places, and they have been so severely deformed and altered that their original character is difficult to determine.

The record of the succeeding Mesozoic era, though lacking in many details, is much more complete. Thick sedimentary deposits, including limestone, shale, and sandstone, were laid down in the northern part of the region, and some contain Triassic fossils, testimony to a marine invasion of this part of Alaska about 155 to 185 million years ago.

Vigorous and long-continued volcanic eruptions then took place, early in Jurassic time. Countless volcanoes burst into activity, especially in the eastern part of the region, discharging ash and lava in vast quantities. The presence among these volcanic deposits of thin layers of tuffaceous sandstone, shale, and conglomerate shows that at least part of the volcanic material was laid down in bodies of water. Farther west, where the volcanic rocks are several thousands of feet thick, fragmental ejecta are subordinate to thick, massive lava flows, proof that the volcanoes there were of a less explosive type.

Normal conditions of sedimentation were resumed in middle Jurassic time, when first sandstone and then shale and shaly sandstone were deposited in a shallow sea. The outstanding event of Mesozoic time in this region, however, was the intrusion of tremendous bodies of granite into the earth's crust. In the western Talkeetna Mountains, a single intrusion occupies 1,400 square miles, and its buried extent is doubtless much greater. The prevailing coarse-grained texture of these intrusive rocks indicates that the igneous melt from which they crystallized cooled slowly far beneath the surface, but the mechanics by which such vast quantities of molten rock were emplaced are not well understood. In the Talkeetna Mountains alone the volume of the intrusive bodies is certainly many hundreds of cubic miles. An equal volume of invaded rocks must, therefore, have been either displaced or absorbed into the molten mass, but the evidence is too scanty to show to what extent the older rocks may have been uparched or pushed aside.

After the sedimentary beds of middle Jurassic age had been laid down, they were tilted, uplifted, and subjected to erosion. Then, in late Jurassic time, they were partly submerged and several hundreds of feet of conglomerate and more than a thousand feet of finer sediments were deposited on top of them.

Shallow seas again invaded the southeastern part of the region in early Cretaceous time, and explosive volcanoes erupted on adjacent lands. These events are recorded in a series of conglomerates and tuffs, overlain by a few hundred feet of limestone in the headwaters of the Matanuska River. At about the same time, another arm of the sea flooded the northern border of the region, leaving a thick succession of nonfossiliferous muds and sandstones.

Probably all the Talkeetna Mountains had emerged from the sea by the end of early Cretaceous time, and they have remained above sea level ever since. During late Cretaceous time, erosion reduced the region to moderate relief, and great quantities of granitic debris accumulated as conglomerate, shale, and sandstone along the southern margin of the present mountains. At approximately the same time, in the northern part of the region, there was extensive intrusion of granitic rocks and outpouring of acidic lavas.

These events were followed by a long spell of erosion during which the mountains were subdued once more and the adjacent basins were filled with detritus. Lowering of the land reduced the gradients of the streams, so that they gradually lost their power to transport coarse detritus and could carry only small loads of finer sediment. Broad swamps then developed within which peat accumulated, eventually to be transformed into the coal beds now to be found in the Matanuska Valley.

The period of slow erosion and peat accumulation was brought to an end in mid-Tertiary time by renewed uplift. Invigorated streams then began to erode more rapidly, carrying coarse gravel to the lowlands to bury the great deposits of sand, clay, and peat to a depth of as much as 3,000 feet. Once more, as erosion went on, the relief of the region became fairly gentle. Extensive sheets of basaltic lava were then poured out in the central part, and explosive eruptions laid down tuffs and breccias there, while thin sills and dikes of lava were injected underground, along fractures and between the layers of older rocks. The close of Tertiary time was marked by general uplift of the Talkeetna area, after which the highlands were deeply dissected by streams to approximately their present relief.

When the Pleistocene period began about a million years ago, the valleys in the Talkeetna Mountains were V-shaped in cross section, and the streams followed somewhat sinuous courses as they swung between opposing spurs on the valley walls. Then the climate became cooler and wetter. The snow line crept down the mountainsides and glaciers formed at the heads of every stream valley, growing in length and thickness from year to year. Despite fluctuations, the cumulative effect through many centuries was for the glaciers to extend ever farther, filling the valleys ever deeper, until by coalescing in the lower basins and overflowing valley walls a very large part of the region was buried beneath a mass of slowly moving ice thousands of feet in thickness. Finally, all the lowlands below 3,000 or 4,000 feet were completely buried beneath a vast, nearly level plain of ice, and all the mountain valleys were brimful of tributary glaciers. Only the steep, sharp crests of ridges projected through the immense white mantle. It was a bleak, forbidding sight.

Then the climate became milder and the ice began a fluctuating retreat. The landscape the glaciers left in their wake was profoundly different from that which had been present before. The valleys were no longer V-shaped in cross section but U-shaped, their walls rising precipitously from broad, flat floors. No longer were the valleys sinuous; now they were straight troughs or bent in great sweeping curves so that the view up and down them was open for miles. Tributaries joined the main streams by plunging in falls and cataracts from hanging valleys where thinner glaciers had been unable to carve their floors as deeply as did the trunk glaciers in the principal valleys.

In other ways also the ice-carved mountains contrasted with those sculptured earlier by flowing waters. Now, armchair-shaped valley heads, truncated spurs on valley walls, sawtooth ridges, rock-basin lakes, and great, bare cliffs of rock proclaimed the erosive power of the Pleistocene glaciers.

Glaciers have by no means completely disappeared from the Talkeetna Mountains. Several of them, between 6 and 10 miles in length, and many smaller ones survive in the southeastern part. The largest glaciers feed the southward-flowing Chickaloon River and the headwaters of the Talkeetna River and its northwestward-flowing tributaries, Sheep River and Iron Creek. Several small ice fields lie in the headwaters of the westward-flowing Kashwitna River.

The traveler by air will note as he flies over the Talkeetna Mountains that the jagged ridges, which rise from the deep troughlike valleys, all reach approximately the same height; in other words, the summits are strikingly accordant. In the southeastern part they reach elevations of 6,000 to 7,000 feet; to the north and west they are somewhat lower. A corresponding gradual change is apparent in the form of the ridges; the higher ones in the southeastern part are razor-sharp, but as the general level decreases, the ridge tops become flat or rounded, until on the western flank of the mountains all of them are rounded and subdued. These changes record the fact that the lower ridges, because they were entirely overridden by the great Pleistocene ice sheets, were not subjected to the sapping action that affected the higher ridges that rose above the level of the ice.

The Talkeetna Mountains present not only a wealth of alpine topography cut in a large variety of rocks, but they give promise of considerable mineral wealth. The Willow Creek district, in the southwestern part, was for many years second in Alaska in production of lode gold. Several mines and numerous prospects were opened on the headwaters of Willow Creek and the Little Susitna River in a mineralized zone at least 8 miles long in the quartz diorite of the great Talkeetna batholith. This is in a region directly accessible by roads connecting with the Glenn Highway at Palmer in the lower Matanuska Valley. Small amounts of placer gold, copper, antimony, and silver have also been found at various places, enough to indicate the presence of valuable minerals that may some day be developed.

FARRELL F. BARNES

Cook Inlet–Susitna Lowland

Cook Inlet is a long, narrow embayment in the south coast of Alaska, bordered on the east by the Kenai Peninsula and on the west by the south end of the Alaska Range. Near its mouth, high mountains rise boldly from the water's edge. North of Kachemak Bay the inlet is bordered by cliffs, a few hundred feet high, forming the wave-cut edge of a rolling lowland that extends eastward 30 or 40 miles to the base of the Kenai Mountains. This lowland is underlain, at least in part, by coal-bearing beds of Tertiary age that form conspicuous exposures along the shore. The surface is covered by glacial deposits and by stream and terrace gravels. Across the inlet similar lowlands, or piedmont plains, extend westward to the base of the Alaska Range. Lowlands also extend east and north of Point Campbell, between Turnagain Arm and Knik Arm and north of Knik Arm and the head of the inlet, where they merge into the Susitna lowland.

All these lowlands have a common origin. All are at least partly floored by sedimentary rocks of Tertiary age and have been overridden by a great glacier that descended the Susitna Valley and Cook Inlet, fed by many tributaries from the mountains to the east and west. Their topography is due partly to the erosive action of those glaciers, and partly to deposition of moraine and of gravel from glacial streams. Upper Cook Inlet is shallow;

43

indeed, a filling of about 200 feet would completely exclude the ocean from the part above Kachemak Bay, and the lowlands east and west of the upper inlet would then be continuous with those of the Susitna Valley. Such a filling is now in progress. The deltas of the Susitna, Matanuska, and Knik rivers and the head of Turnagain Arm are rapidly encroaching upon the area of tidewater, and the wide expanse of mud flats, visible at low tide in the upper inlet, testifies to the great volume of detritus being carried by glacial streams to the sea.

The broad Susitna lowland, the landward continuation of the Cook Inlet depression, is a structural basin comprising the lowland basins of the Susitna River and its tributaries and of several other rivers that flow directly into the head of the inlet. It is bordered on the south by Cook Inlet, on the east by the Chugach and the Talkeetna Mountains, and on the southwest, west, and north by the Alaska Range. The main basin so bounded has a length of about 100 miles from north to south and a width of more than 50 miles in the latitude of the Kashwitna River, but narrows to the north. The entire Cook Inlet–Susitna lowland, extending from the mouth of Kachemak Bay into the Chulitna Valley, is more than 200 miles long and averages about 60 miles wide, although within that area lie the waters of upper Cook Inlet and some mountains that project above the level of the rolling plain.

Branching arms project from the main lowland far into the surrounding mountains, the largest and most important of these being the Matanuska Valley, south of the Talkeetna Mountains, which contains much of the best agricultural land and the only commercially exploited bituminous coal deposits in Alaska. The Susitna River flows east of the center of the basin, parallel to the west base of the Talkeetna Mountains at a distance of about 8 miles. The river itself occupies a flood plain that ranges from 1 to 6 or 8 miles in width, and the bordering lowland is surfaced with glacial deposits and stream gravels and dotted with abundant lakes. Closer to the mountains the tributary streams are more deeply entrenched so that the rolling topography of the lowland gives way to steeper slopes.

When and how the great structural depression occupied by the Cook Inlet–Susitna lowland was formed is not fully known. All that can be said with assurance is that toward the end of Cretaceous time, or possibly at the beginning of the Tertiary period, roughly 60 million years ago, this great lowland already existed and its extent was essentially the same as at present. Rocks of much greater age are to be seen in various places, but our knowledge of the landscapes of these earlier times is too scant to show precisely when and how the lowland first came into being. The oldest rocks of wide extent are nonmarine coal-bearing deposits of Eocene age, and these tell the following story.

As the preëxisting mountains were slowly worn down by erosion and the lowlands were filled with their detritus, the gradients of the streams became gentler. Hence not only was less sediment transported to the lowlands, but generally it was finer-grained. Sand and mud were no longer laid down continuously; now they were laid down spasmodically, and there were long intervals when vegetation grew and died to form successive layers of peat. Organic accumulation alternated with deposition of sand and clay, and the deeply buried layers of peat were gradually changed to beds of coal. No doubt the time required for the formation of these coals was very long, for erosion of the highlands supplying the interbedded sediments was slow, and each foot of coal necessitated the accumulation of many feet of loose, uncompressed peat. At no time was the entire lowland covered by peat bogs; there were always some parts where detritus was being deposited by streams. It is difficult, therefore, to correlate coal beds and sedimentary deposits that are widely separated.

From time to time throughout this early Tertiary period there were mild volcanic eruptions, and small areas were inundated by flows of basaltic lava. These eruptions, however, were only the feeble beginning of the intense volcanic activity of later times.

Deposition of the coal-bearing formation, at least in the Matanuska Valley, was ended by uplift of the Talkeetna Mountains in middle Tertiary time. The rejuvenated streams began at once to erode their valleys more actively, and coarse gravel was carried to the lowlands to cover the widespread deposits of sand, clay, and peat there. Locally, gravel accumulated to a thickness of 3,000 feet. Filling of the lowlands and lowering of the mountains combined to reduce the region to one of gentle slopes. Then followed a period of intense volcanic activity. Extensive sheets of basaltic lava poured over the area now occupied by the central Talkeetna Mountains, layers of tuff and breccia were produced by explosions, and molten igneous material was intruded as dikes and sills, especially into the coal-bearing beds of the Matanuska Valley.

By the end of Tertiary time, mountain-building processes had in large part ceased. The major highlands, including the Chugach and the Talkeetna Mountains and the Alaska Range, had been raised to approximately their present height, and the Cook Inlet–Susitna basin existed much as it is today. But whereas the dominant topographic units were already defined, their sculpture was very different from what we see now, for it had been developed by stream erosion in a temperate climate. The area now occupied by Cook Inlet was somewhat narrower, and the bordering lowlands were better drained, had fewer lakes, and were probably dissected by more or less equally spaced stream valleys separated by low rolling hills and ridges. Turnagain Arm was then in all likelihood the valley of a mountain stream, and perhaps Knik Arm was also a stream valley above the reach of the tides. At its north end Cook Inlet may have extended many miles over the area now occupied by the lowland delta.

It is still impossible to reconstruct accurately the courses of even the main rivers as they flowed at the end of the Tertiary period, but certainly the drainage was very different from that of the present. A great river emptied into the sea at some point along what is now Cook Inlet. This ancient river was much larger than the present Susitna, for it received waters not only from the area now tributary to the Susitna, but in all likelihood it also drained the upper part of the Copper River basin and those parts of the south slopes of the Alaska Range that now drain to the Tanana by way of the Nenana and the Delta rivers.

The final event that gave the Cook Inlet–Susitna lowland essentially its present aspect was the Pleistocene glaciation. As the mountain glaciers slowly grew, they pushed beyond the mountain fronts into the lowlands, especially on the Pacific slope, where precipitation was heaviest and the spread of the glaciers was, therefore, most rapid. Tongues of ice from the Kenai Mountains, the Chugach Range, and the Talkeetna Mountains pushed westward into the lowland to coalesce with other tongues from the Alaska Range to the west and north. At the same time ice from the Copper River basin overflowed into the heads of the Susitna and Matanuska rivers.

The Cook Inlet–Susitna Glacier at the time of its maximum extent was limited in size only by the margins of the basin. It extended from near the crest line of one bordering range almost to the summit of the opposite mountains. It was margined on the west and north by the crest of the Alaska Range, and eastward it was continuous with the Copper River Glacier. The Talkeetna Mountains sent down radiating glaciers in all directions, and these contributed their ice to the Susitna Glacier either directly or by way of the Copper River basin or the Matanuska Valley. Similarly the Chugach Mountains sent ice to the Susitna Glacier through the Matanuska Valley, and down what are now Knik and Turnagain arms, and other tributary glaciers flowed down from the Kenai Mountains. Just how far down Cook Inlet the Susitna Glacier was able to advance has not been determined, but it certainly reached the forelands south of Turnagain Arm, and probably extended all the way to the mouth of the inlet.

At the time of greatest glaciation the entire area south of the crest of the Alaska Range was flooded by a tremendous mass of ice covering all but the highest peaks and ridges. Along the west flank of the Talkeetna Mountains, near the Kashwitna River, the Susitna Glacier at one time reached a height of about 4,000 feet, and the main southward-moving lobe was more than 50 miles wide and had a thickness in the center of the valley of nearly 4,000 feet.

As the great glaciers shrank, the Cook Inlet–Susitna lowland gradually took on its present form. It was no longer well-drained, but covered with a continuous blanket of morainal deposits and outwash gravels enclosing innumerable lakes and swamps. In the upper part of the Matanuska Valley the effects of glaciation were mainly erosional; ice-scoured ridges of hard intrusive rocks were left in bold relief by removal of the softer surrounding sediments. In the lower part of the valley, on the contrary, the effects of glaciation were mainly depositional; there the glaciers left hummocks and looping ridges of morainal debris, and their meltwaters left outwash deposits ranging from a few feet to a few hundreds of feet in thickness. Productive soil has developed on the less rugged parts of these deposits, so that today the landscape of the lower Matanuska Valley, as well as parts of the Kenai lowland east of Lower Cook Inlet, includes the fields and farmsteads of some of the latest, and perhaps the last, agricultural pioneers of the nation.

CLYDE WAHRHAFTIG

The Alaska Range

The Alaska Range is a great arcuate mountain wall, about 600 miles long, which extends entirely across the Territory. At its eastern end it is separated from the Wrangell and the St. Elias Mountains only by narrow trenchlike depressions and passes, and at its opposite end it merges imperceptibly with the Aleutian Range. It encircles an area of lowlands and mountains tributary to the Pacific Ocean, separating them from the great interior region of lowlands and highlands of central Alaska, which drain to the Bering Sea. The Alaska Range is about 30 miles wide near the Canadian boundary, and widens gradually westward for the next 470 miles until in the vicinity of Mount McKinley it is 60 miles wide, and in the vicinity of Mount Spurr it is 120 miles wide. Throughout its length the range is rugged and intensely glaciated.

Although the highest mountain on the North American continent—Mount McKinley, 20,300 feet high—lies within the Alaska Range, the number of really high mountains in the range is comparatively small. Fewer than twenty peaks exceed 10,000 feet in height, and the crest of most of the range averages between 7,000 and 9,000 feet in altitude. Consequently, the few high mountains that directly adjoin the bordering lowlands present a towering aspect and are much more impressive than if they were merely the culminating elevations of a range more nearly uniform in height. The steep north face of Mount McKinley is 15,000 feet high, and the opposite face is even steeper and almost as high; Mounts Foraker, Spurr, Hunter, Hayes, and Deborah are likewise impressive in their isolation, rising by nearly vertical cliffs 5,000 to 10,000 feet above surrounding country.

Four great mountain masses dominate the range: these are the Mount Spurr–Mount Gerdine group in the extreme southwest, culminating in Mount Gerdine (12,600 feet); the Mount McKinley group at the great bend in the range, culminating in Mount McKinley and Mount Foraker (17,280 feet); the Mount Hayes group near longitude 147° West, culminating in Mount Hayes (13,470 feet) and Mount Deborah (12,540 feet); and the mountains around Mount Kimball (9,680 feet) at longitude 145° West.

These four mountain masses, and a few intervening peaks, are centers from which great glaciers radiate; they are largely sheathed in ice and snow, winter and summer, and gleam white upon the horizon. Although by far the most impressive and stupendous parts of the range, they are inhospitable and barren; the crevasses of their glaciers combined with frequent rockfalls and avalanches make them dangerous to penetrate. On clear days they are regions of intense brightness and strong contrasts; indeed the whiteness of their snow and ice is so dazzling that protruding rocks seem dark or almost black. The adjacent lowlands and the low parts of the range, on the other hand, are regions of life where erosion, although rapid by usual standards, is slow enough to be no more than an inconvenience instead of a hazard.

Despite the fact that the Alaska Range is the great mountain barrier between the Pacific Coast and the interior lowland, only from Mount McKinley National Park southwestward does it form a continuous drainage divide. Six rivers, beginning with the Nenana and extending to the eastern end of the range just beyond the Canadian border, rise in the lowlands south of the mountains and flow northward across the range to empty into the Yukon or the Tanana. They are, from west to east, the Nenana River, Delta River, Nabesna River, Chisana River, Beaver Creek, and White River. Several of these provide routes of travel across the mountains. The Alaska Railroad, for example, follows the Nenana across the range; the Richardson Highway follows the Delta, and the White River was used by gold seekers as a trail from the lower Copper River country to the Klondike. In addition to these rivers, several low passes cross the range, among them being Rainy Pass, about 2,500 feet high, across the southwestern part of the range, which was a route of travel in dog-sled days between Cook Inlet and the Kuskokwim country. Another pass, the Mentasta, in the eastern part of the range, was followed by the old Eagle trail and telegraph line, and is now used by the Glenn Highway.

The region south of Rainy Pass is one of the least explored areas of Alaska. Until the Geological Survey expeditions of 1927–1929, led by Stephen R. Capps, it was almost entirely unknown. Capps, when exploring the headwaters of the Skwentna, Stony, and Chakachatna rivers, discovered a land of rugged mountains carved by glaciers and frost action into narrow pinnacles and spires of tremendous height, and between these mountains deep river canyons, many of them connected by low passes that break the mountains into separate blocks and afford the only routes of travel through the range. Capps also found immense glaciers and beautiful lakes, some of which, particularly Lake Clark and Lake Chakachamna, he ranked among the most beautiful bodies of water in the world. The mountains, although visible from Anchorage and the Alaska Railroad on a clear day, are separated from Cook Inlet by a wide belt of marshy lowlands covered with impenetrable thickets of alder bushes. They lie in a region of frequent storms, and the rivers that drain them are swift and dangerous.

The eastern side of the group of mountains just described receives the greatest precipitation; hence the largest glaciers are to be found there, for example, the Capps and Triumvirate glaciers, which descend from the east flanks of Mounts Spurr and Gerdine. Farther west the precipitation diminishes and the present glaciers are much smaller, although all of the mountains were intensely glaciated during the Pleistocene period. The lowlands on the west side of the mountains, because they are less marshy and more open than those on the opposite side, provide the easiest access to the interior trails entering the Stony River basin from Lake Clark on the south, and up the upper Kuskokwim from Farewell Landing Field on the north.

The greatest concentration of high mountains in the Alaska Range, culminating in Mount McKinley, occurs north of Rainy Pass and in the region extending northward for about half the length of Mount McKinley National Park. Although far more rugged and more precipitous than those to the south, these mountains are much better explored and more often visited, chiefly because Mount McKinley and the neighboring peaks are a challenge to climbers. The core of the region consists of an almost continuous network of great valley glaciers, each a mile to 5 miles wide, meandering between snow- and ice-clad mountains that tower above them, cliff on cliff, to heights of 1 to 3 miles. The glaciers on the south side of the range, for example, Ruth, Tokachitna, and Kahiltna glaciers, which are 40 to 50 miles long, descend to altitudes of less than 1,000 feet above sea level, the lowest few miles of their lengths being mantled by rock-debris. On the north side of the range, the glaciers are much smaller and shorter, only the Muldrow, nearly 40 miles long, comparing in size with the giants on the south side. They extend to the edge of a plain, 2,000 to 3,000 feet above sea level, and they are debris-covered for long distances above their lower ends.

Along the south side of the range, the high mountains, although rising impressively above Susitna Valley, are separated by a belt of foothills and lower mountains that gradually increase in height over a distance of 25 to 30 miles to the highest peaks. Spectacular views of Mount McKinley can be had from the Alaska Railroad at Talkeetna and Hurricane, from Curry Lookout, 4 miles by trail west of Curry, and from many places in the Peters Hills. On the north side, the mountains rise much more abruptly from the plain, and the North Peak of Mount McKinley, 19,000 feet high, lies no more than 10 miles from a lowland plain only 3,000 feet in height.

The stupendous mountain wall with which the Alaska Range here faces the Tanana-Kuskokwim lowland is complicated by a glacier-filled trough parallel to the front of the range 5 to 10 miles southward within the mountains. This trough marks a great fault which can be traced continuously across Alaska from east of the Canadian border to beyond the headwaters of the Kuskokwim, and probably continues southwestward through the Ahklun Mountains to Bristol Bay. It separates a group of lower northern foothills, largely glacier-free and to a considerable extent unglaciated, from the great ice-clad mountain wall to the south. The upper part of the Muldrow Glacier lies within this trench (see pl. 12); the glaciers west of it, however, cross the trench and the adjacent foothill range to deploy on to the bordering lowland.

A relatively low segment of the Alaska Range extends eastward from the Mount McKinley group for about 75 miles to the high mountains of the Mount Hayes group. This low segment merges with the high mountains around Mount McKinley, and the overlapping group of rolling foothills is known as the Kantishna Hills. The western border of this low segment is along the lower part of the Muldrow Glacier and Anderson Pass; its eastern border is near the Yanert Glacier. Few peaks in this part of the range are higher than 8,000 feet. Glaciers are scarce and small and are confined for the most part to north-facing cirques and the heads of valleys. Although much of this country is above timber line, large parts of the mountains, even above timber line, are coated with turf. Along its north side, this part of the range has a belt of low foothills 15 to 25 miles wide, extending from the

Kantishna Hills on the west to the Delta River on the east, consisting of subdued, rolling ridges rarely more than 1,000 or 2,000 feet above the surrounding lowlands.

A striking feature of this segment of the Alaska Range, particularly noticeable from the air, is the pattern of parallel east-west ridges, about 15 miles apart, separated by long narrow valleys. Strangely enough, the drainage does not follow these valleys but has a dendritic pattern roughly at right angles thereto, the rivers cutting directly across ridges and valleys alike. In some places the parallelism of the northward-flowing streams is as conspicuous as that of the ridges and valleys perpendicular to them. Each river as a consequence crosses the range alternately across a lowland in a broad terraced valley and then plunges into a narrow gorge. This makes north-south travel along the rivers much more difficult than east-west travel along the longitudinal lowlands. Hence, except for the Alaska Railroad, which follows the Nenana River, all roads and highways, such as the McKinley Park Highway, follow east-west valleys. The Alaska Railroad crosses the high ridge between McKinley Park Station and Healy in one of the most spectacular gorges along its route, and so is subject to the danger of landslides and rockfalls.

The segment of the Alaska Range just described is the most pleasant, most populated, and among the most scenic of all. It is the part most likely to be seen by the tourist, for it includes the accessible eastern part of Mount McKinley National Park. It also contains the greatest known mineral wealth of the range, including, besides the large coal reserves of the Nenana coal field in the northern foothills, gold, silver, and antimony of the Kantishna and Bonnifield mining districts, and deposits of limestone near Windy.

East of the low segment of the Alaska Range is another area of ice fields, centered in a group of spirelike mountains of which Mount Hayes (13,700 feet) is the highest. This part of the range repeats on a reduced scale the major features of the great ice-sheathed segment that includes Mount McKinley. The headwaters of several large rivers, the Susitna, Delta, Nenana, and Little Delta, are in the mountains around Mount Hayes, Mount Deborah (12,540 feet), and Hess Mountain (12,030 feet), and great glaciers radiate from gathering grounds around those peaks. On some glaciers, such as the Susitna on the south side of the range, moraine ridges have been thrown into fantastic curves by variations in the movement of the ice. Another glacier, the Black Rapids, which descends to the Delta River Valley, made a spectacular advance in 1936, endangering part of the

Plate 1. Parts of the St. Elias Range and Malaspina Glacier. Mount St. Elias (18,008 feet) is the high peak on the far left; Mount Augusta (14,070 feet) is on the far right. The dark, curving bands on the Malaspina Glacier mark outcrops of thrust planes in the ice. (Photograph by Bradford Washburn.)

Plate 2. Hubbard Glacier entering Disenchantment Bay, Yakutat Bay area. Mount Hubbard (14,950 feet), in the distance, is carved from part of the Coast Range batholith; some banded metamorphic rocks are visible in the middle distance. (Photograph by Bradford Washburn.)

Plate 3. Mount Crillon (12,726 feet) and Brady Glacier. View looking west from above Glacier Bay. (Photograph by Bradford Washburn.)

*Plate 4. Mount Crillon (12,726 feet) viewed across
Johns Hopkins Inlet. This is part of the Glacier Bay area. During
the early part of this century there was a dramatic recession
of the glacier that formerly extended far down the inlet.
(Photograph by Bradford Washburn.)*

*Plate 5. Nunatak Fiord, Yakutat Bay. The Nunatak (1,278 feet)
in the foreground. In 1909, as shown in the retouched photograph
(at left) (based on a topographic map by R. S. Tarr and
L. Martin), the ice extended more than 3 miles below its present
limit. (Photograph by Bradford Washburn, 1938.)*

Plate 6. Part of the Chugach Range, including Mount Witherspoon (12,023 feet). View from above Prince William Sound, looking up the Columbia Glacier. (Photograph by Bradford Washburn.)

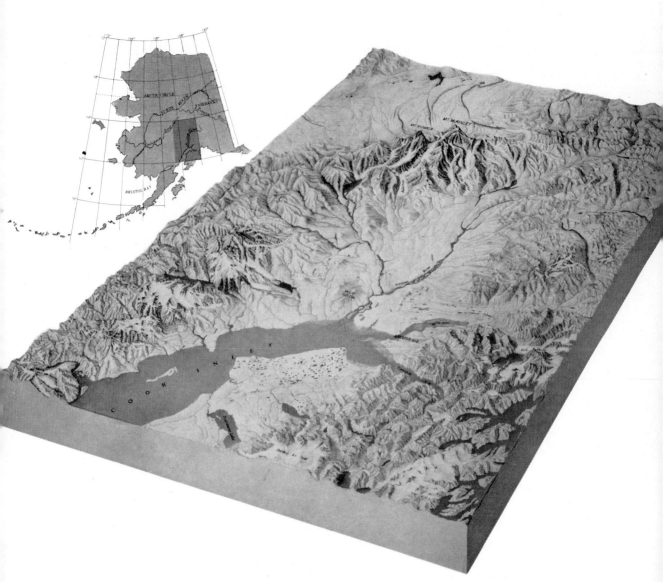

Plate 7. Perspective diagram of Upper Cook Inlet area showing setting of Anchorage.

Plate 8. Mount Sanford and the Wrangell Mountains. View looking south. Mount Sanford (16,208 feet), and Mounts Jarvis and Blackburn, which lie to the left, are extinct volcanoes of late Cenozoic age but Mount Wrangell (14,006 feet), which lies to the right, is still active. The flat, even crests of the narrow ridges between the glaciers are remnants of the original slopes of the Mount Sanford volcano. (Photograph by Bradford Washburn.)

Plate 9. Sourdough Peak in the southern foothills of the Wrangell Mountains. View looking north. The mountain is carved from granite porphyry, which intrudes sandstones and shales belonging to the Kennicott formation of Jurassic and Cretaceous age, a remnant of which forms the sharp, dark summit pinnacle. The lower slopes of the mountain have been smoothed and rounded by a huge glacier that flowed down the Nizina Valley from right to left during the Pleistocene period. The upper part of the mountain has been steepened by frost action both during and since that period. Frost-riving of the upper cliffs resulted in the accumulation of abundant talus on the shelf below. Then, as ice accumulated within the growing talus, the combined thickness became sufficient for the mass to flow slowly down the mountainsides, creating a lavalike tongue of rubble known as a rock glacier. (Photograph by Bradford Washburn.)

Plate 10. Cliffs of Triassic limestone in the southeastern Wrangell Mountains. This section in Chitistone Canyon is between 1,500 and 2,500 feet thick. The famous copper ore bodies of the Kennicott Mine occur within similar limestones. (Photograph by Bradford Washburn.)

Plate 11. Mount McKinley from the northeast. Muldrow and Traleika glaciers to the right and left, respectively. The upper part of the mountain and the right in the foreground are carved from light-colored granite; the darker rocks in the middle distance are folded slates and graywackes, probably of Mesozoic age. The great fault that runs along the entire length of the Alaska Range passes along the Muldrow Glacier and through Gunsight Pass on the right, near where the glacier bends. McGonagall Pass in the foreground. (Photograph by Bradford Washburn.)

Plate 12. Part of the Alaska Range, including Mount McKinley. View looking
southwest. Mount McKinley is 20,300 feet high, but the plain in the right distance
is only about 2,000 feet above sea level. The mountains in the foreground and to
the right, beyond the Teklanika River, vary in altitude between 5,000 and
8,000 feet. Except in the distance, where there are altered submarine basaltic
lavas (greenstones) of Triassic (?) age, these mountains consist of sandstones,
shales, and conglomerates interbedded with brightly colored lava flows ranging
from rhyolites to basalts, all of which are part of the Cantwell formation
of late Cretaceous age. Similar lava flows give the country around
Polychrome Pass its brilliant hues. The flat country lying to the left of these
mountains and stretching parallel to the Alaska Range, is carved from poorly
consolidated sands and gravels of Tertiary age which are folded into a tight
syncline. The Denali Highway follows this valley from near the Teklanika River
to the Muldrow Glacier, crossing a series of passes, including Sable,
Polychrome, Highway, and Thorofare passes which are famous sights in the
National Park. The rivers that head in the main part of the Alaska Range flow
north through this valley and then cut across the low mountains to the north as if
they were not there. Their courses must have been established on a smooth,
north-sloping plain before these mountains were uplifted. The higher parts of the
Alaska Range are covered by ice. During the Pleistocene period, glaciers
extended far to the north of the range along old river valleys, which they carved
into wide, flat-floored troughs. (Photograph by Bradford Washburn.)

*Plate 13. Eocene coals and sandstones on Lignite
Creek, near Healy. Thickest coal bed, 30 feet.
(Photograph by Clyde Wahrhaftig.)*

Plate 14. Recessional moraines on the north side of Iliamna volcano. These curved moraines were left by the spasmodic retreat of the glacier seen in the background. (Photograph by Bradford Washburn.)

Plate 15. Caldera of Katmai volcano. View looking northwest across the caldera formed in 1912 by collapse of the top of the volcano as a result of eruptions in the adjacent Valley of Ten Thousand Smokes. Knife Peak volcano in the distance must be considered dormant rather than extinct, for the horizontal plume issuing from its upper slopes comes from a hot fumarole. (Photograph by Adolph Murie, 1951.)

Plate 16. Head of the Valley of Ten Thousand Smokes. View looking southwest to Mageik volcano. The sharp peak in the middle distance is Falling Mountain. All of the valley head in the foreground, including the hummocky top of the glacier at the extreme left, is thickly mantled by ash erupted from vents to the vicinity in 1912. (Photograph by Garniss Curtis.)

Plate 17. Dacite dome on the south flank of Trident volcano. This dome was formed in 1953 near the head of the Valley of Ten Thousand Smokes, and remained active until 1954. Here one sees viscous lava creeping down slowly from the summit vent. When this picture was taken, the dome was about 300 feet high. Subsequently a long flow extended southward from it into the valley of the Katmai River, part of which is visible in the background. (Photograph by Garniss Curtis.)

Plate 18. Shishaldin volcano, Unimak Island. This beautifully symmetrical volcano has erupted steam and ash many times since its first recorded activity in 1775. Isanotski and Roundtop volcanoes, also on Unimak Island, rise behind it. Roundtop has probably erupted several times since records have been kept of Alaskan volcanism, and Isanotski may also have been active during that period. (Photograph by U. S. Navy, October, 1942.)

Plate 19. Placer gold mining near Fairbanks. The artificial cliffs in the distance reveal frozen "muck" containing vegetal matter. The muck has been stripped to expose the underlying gold-bearing gravels for mining. The moving dredge leaves neatly stacked dumps in its wake.

(Photograph by Bradford Washburn.)

Plate 20. Typical upland terrain, northern Seward Peninsula. Permafrost underlies most of the area, and the bedrocks are mostly schists. The rounded landforms result from slow downcreep of the soil mantle caused mainly by alternate freezing and thawing. (Photograph by U. S. Air Force, October, 1946.)

*Plate 21. Mount Doonerak from Amawk Mountain, Brooks Range.
The Upper North Fork of Koyukuk River occupies the center
of the picture; the distant mountains are part of or close to the
Arctic Divide. The Brooks Range here consists of bedded
Paleozoic sedimentary rocks, largely of Devonian age.
(Photograph by Robert Marshall.)*

Plate 22. Highest part of the Brooks Range. View from south of Mount Michelson. This typically glacial landscape is carved from slates, quartzites, and schists, probably of early Paleozoic age. (Photograph by U. S. Navy, July, 1949.)

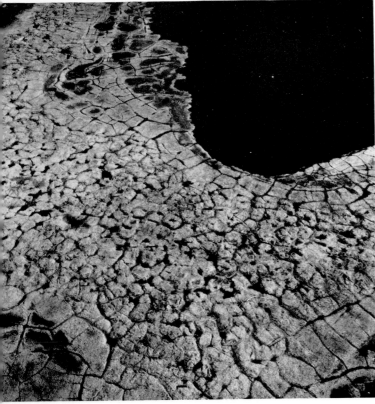

Plate 23. Polygonal ground and thaw lakes near Skull Cliff, southwest of Barrow. The upper picture shows the parallel alignment of the lakes. (Photograph by U. S. Navy.)

Richardson Highway and the Black Rapids Lodge, and reminding us that Alaska is still in an ice age.

The continuity of the Alaska Range is broken by the broad valley of the Delta River, another stream that rises on the south side of the range and flows north across it to the Tanana. The Delta is followed through the range by the Richardson Highway, the oldest motor road in this part of Alaska. Immediately to the east are ice-clad mountains almost as high as those to the west, the highest being Mount Kimball, about 10,000 feet above sea level. Great glaciers descend from these mountains to the plains on the south side and for some distance down the canyons on the north side. Three of these glaciers, the Gulkana, Canwell, and Castner, are visible from the Richardson Highway. The segment of snow-clad peaks and giant glaciers, from the Yanert on the west to the glaciers at the head of the Tok River on the east, is 120 miles long, and is broken near the middle by the canyon of the Delta River.

The easternmost part of the Alaska Range extends from the head of the Tok River to the Canadian border. This also is a relatively low part of the range, and the few glaciers confined to the higher parts of the valleys and to north-facing cirques are small. The range is here broken into segments by several low passes and by the valleys of two great rivers, the Nabesna and the Chisana. The segment between Mentasta Pass and Nabesna River has been called the Mentasta Mountains, and the one extending from the Nabesna to the Canadian border has been called the Nutzotin Mountains. Those names were applied by the early explorers Brooks and Schrader when they saw the mountains at a distance and, having only an imperfect knowledge of the topography, thought that they were separated from the Alaska Range by a great lowland through which the Eagle-Valdez trail was supposed to pass. When this trail was discovered to follow a narrow valley surrounded by high mountains, it became apparent that all the mountains formed parts of a single great range.

Two contrasting types of scenery prevail in these mountains. Where the highest peaks do not exceed 6,500 feet, mountain slopes, although steep, are even, and none of the summits are sharp. Timber line is at about 3,000 feet, so that the lower slopes of most of the mountains are clothed in forest. Most of the rocks are dark sedimentary and volcanic types, chiefly of Paleozoic age, and the mountains have a somber aspect. Such, to a large extent, are the mountains around Mentasta Pass, the route of the Glenn Highway. The central, higher parts of the Nutzotin and the Mentasta Mountains, on the other hand, are made up of thinly bedded rocks of Mesozoic age which weather characteristically into craggy peaks. There the mountains are extremely rugged, with sharp ridges and peaks and steep broken slopes. They include Mount Allen (9,500 feet), the highest of the Nutzotin Mountains, and many peaks about 8,000 feet which are the gathering grounds of small glaciers. That part of the Alaska Range rises sharply above the Tanana Valley on the north, forming an impressive mountain wall. It is separated from the much higher Wrangell Mountains on the southwest by only a narrow valley and a series of low narrow passes. To the traveler flying between Whitehorse and Fairbanks or Anchorage, the eastern part of the Alaska Range seems to be hardly more than a foothill belt of the Wrangell Mountains.

The rocks that make up the Alaska Range are of great variety and represent periods of the earth's history from the most ancient to the most recent. Both sedimentary and igneous types are widespread. Some of the most ancient sedimentary rocks have been subjected to repeated mountain-building forces and have thus been converted to schists; however, the youngest of the folded sedimentary rocks, which are coal-bearing deposits of Tertiary age, are so slightly consolidated that they erode easily to badlands.

When the early geologists explored the Alaska Range they were surprised to discover that, broadly speaking, the range is carved from a great downfold in the earth's crust—a synclinorium—in which the youngest rocks lie along the center and are flanked on the north and south by older rocks. This relationship clearly implies that the belt occupied by the younger rocks, although now the crest of the range, was once lower than the bordering belts of older rocks.

One of the tasks of geologists in recent years has been to decipher the events that changed this great downfold to the present mighty mountain range, and although much of the history has been worked out, the basic causes remain a matter for speculation. Great longitudinal faults parallel to the range are associated with the downfold. The most extensive of these, as noted already, has been traced almost the entire width of Alaska; at its east end it lies on the north side of the range, then crosses to the south side near Mentasta Pass, and crosses again to the north side at Anderson Pass. It is marked by a narrow trench cut in easily eroded, crushed rocks. Study of the formations on opposite sides of the fault shows that intermittent movements have taken place along it for more than 50 million years, and there is evidence that movements still continue.

The oldest formation of the Alaska Range is of Precambrian age and is called the Birch Creek schist. It consists largely of interlocking crystals of quartz and thin sheets of mica, and hence has a pronounced platy structure or schistosity which causes it to weather into thin slabs parallel to the mica flakes. Locally the formation contains limestone, limy schist, and garnetiferous schist. It has been intensely contorted; indeed in many outcrops numerous small folds may be seen within the space of a few feet. On fresh surfaces the schist is gray to greenish-gray, but on weathering its colors change to rusty-brown and pinkish, and most mountains of which it is composed have colors of light brown or tan. The schist forms a band along the north side of the Alaska Range, from the Kantishna Hills on the west to the Tetling River on the east. The band is widest, nearly 30 miles across, near the Richardson Highway; elsewhere its width averages 15 to 20 miles.

Studies in other parts of Alaska indicate that the Birch Creek schist is the oldest rock in the entire Territory, and probably one of the oldest in North America. Its mineral and chemical composition and the presence within it of layers of limestone and black carbonaceous material signify that originally the rocks were sediments washed from still older highlands and deposited in an ancient sea.

North of the Birch Creek schist is a belt about 100 miles long and 15 to 20 miles wide, extending from the east end of the Kantishna Hills to the Little Delta River, composed of different schist and of gneiss, of uncertain age though probably younger. This formation, called the Totatlanika schist from its outcrops along the river of that name, consists of orthoclase, quartz, and mica, a striking feature being the large size of the orthoclase crystals, some of which measure as much as an inch across and several inches long. To judge by its chemical composition, this schist may be an altered rhyolitic lava or ash. Mountains composed of it are pale yellow, but many outcrops and slide-rock slopes are covered with black lichens.

The bedded rocks next younger than these ancient schists are of Paleozoic age. They form great bands flanking a central belt of rocks of Mesozoic age, and locally they extend continuously across the Alaska Range. Their structure is complex; fossils are scarce, and most of the rock types have a monotonous similarity. The oldest members of the group are of Devonian age; the youngest are of Permian age. They include large bodies of limestone interbedded with slate, schist, argillite, and considerable quantities of altered basaltic volcanic rocks called greenstones. One of the most striking units is a discontinuous band of limestone that extends from the railroad at Windy westward for about 50 miles along the crest of the range in Mount

McKinley National Park. The same limestone may also be present near the head of the Yanert Glacier. Most of these Paleozoic rocks have somber colors and make up dark, forbidding mountains, like those around Mentasta Lake and those at the head of the Toklat River. The greenstones, once submarine lava flows and sheets of molten material injected between the sedimentary layers, are mostly dark green or purple but locally, as at Rainbow Mountain on the Richardson Highway, they weather to bright orange, red, and brown.

Still younger than the great mass of Paleozoic sedimentary and volcanic rocks is a formation of Triassic age, approximately 150 to 180 million years old. This also contains abundant greenstones derived from basaltic lava flows. Coeval greenstones are widespread throughout south-central Alaska. In the Copper River country, where they have been called the Nikolai greenstones, they contain appreciable amounts of the metal.

When the greenstones were laid down Alaska was either an immense lava field like the Columbia River plateau of today or, more probably, it was occupied by submarine and island volcanoes of vast extent. The greenstones now form a band along the south side of the range between Mount Hayes and the Toklat River, and in the center of the range near the Toklat River, and probably they crop out also in the mountains south of Valdez Creek. The accustomed eye can readily distinguish them even from afar because they usually from dark-green or dark-brown mountains with rough, jagged slopes. Panorama Mountain across the Nenana River from the Alaska Railroad at Windy is typical, and so are the mountains north of the McKinley Park Highway through Highway Pass and Thorofare Pass. Associated with the greenstones are red and green cherts and argillites, as well as limestones, all of which tend to produce mountains of striking color, with sharp angular forms.

After the eruption of the vast sheets of early Triassic lava, there occurred one of the major periods of mountain-building in the Alaska Range, with accompanying large-scale intrusion of granitic rocks. This was not however the deformation that gave the range its characteristic downfolded, synclinal structure.

The newly elevated mountains were then worn down and submerged beneath the sea. Great volumes of mud and sand, derived partly from the southeast and south, and probably also from the north, were then deposited on the sea bottom where the Alaska Range now stands. Today these sediments are represented by interbedded argillites and graywackes in a monotonous succession. They form the central part of the Nutzotin and the Mentasta Mountains, are widely distributed throughout the Alaska Range southwest of the Alaska Railroad, and probably form the bulk of the range near Rainy Pass. They have been tightly folded, much faulted, intruded by igneous rocks, and injected with many quartz veins, so that it is almost impossible to unravel the details of their structure. Some of the rocks are finely banded, alternate layers of sandstone and shale measuring only an inch or two in thickness; elsewhere, the banding is much coarser. Because the rocks are predominantly dark gray they form drab, somber landscapes. Where they are free from granitic intrusions they are carved into rugged, spectacular scenery, as in the central Nutzotin Mountains, but where the more easily eroded granites are present among them the mountain forms are subdued.

After deposition and intrusion of the foregoing rocks, mighty mountain-building forces again affected the area. Once more the rocks were intensely deformed, and again large volumes of them were displaced by bodies of magma that slowly cooled and solidified far beneath the surface to form new batholiths and stocks. The greatest of these intrusions lies in the extreme southwestern part of the Alaska Range, stretching from the headwaters of Skwentna River southward beyond the south boundary of the range. It extends across the entire width of the Alaska Range, there at its broadest, and underlies thousands of square miles of rugged mountainous country. Several elliptical and elongated bodies of granitic rock occur in the Mount McKinley area, and eastward beyond Mount Hayes. One body underlies both Mount McKinley and Mount Hunter, and another forms Mount Foraker; a third makes up the foothills north of the Muldrow Glacier as far east as Mount Eielson. Other granitic bodies compose the mountains between the Yanert and Nenana glaciers, those between the Wood and Little Delta rivers, part of Mount Deborah, and the mountains south of the Black Rapids Glacier. Bodies of similar granitic rock, from 3 to 5 miles wide and 10 to 20 miles long, also occur in many places in the eastern Alaska Range.

Most of the granitic rocks are light gray, many have a slightly pink cast, and some, entirely devoid of dark minerals, are almost white. They are coarsely crystalline, so that grains of quartz, feldspar, and either mica or hornblende can be readily recognized. Locally the feldspars form large crystals scattered through the finer-grained matrix, and usually they can be detected by flashes of sunlight from their cleavage faces. Of all the rocks in the Alaska Range, these granites are the most resistant to erosion. They are broken only by widely spaced cracks, many of which are vertical. When water freezes in the cracks, the rocks are pried apart and gradually disintegrate, this being the chief mechanism of weathering in the arctic. The resulting granite mountains are, therefore, marked by sharp pinnacles or great domes bounded by sheer cliffs. Nowhere else in Alaska—or in all of America for that matter—are jagged spires and mighty cliffs as abundant as they are here. Greatest of all are Mount McKinley and Mount Hunter and the spires between the Ruth and Tokachitna glaciers southeast of them.

After intrusion of the granitic batholiths, the Alaska Range was eroded once more to a gentle lowland. The rocks that formerly covered the batholiths were stripped over large areas, and the granites thus exposed were partly buried by sediments and volcanic deposits. These sediments, unlike earlier ones, were not laid down beneath the sea, but on land and chiefly by rivers. Among them are conglomerates, sandstones, and shales, and a few beds of coal containing abundant remains of fossil plants. These rocks, called the Cantwell formation, occupy a synclinal area 75 miles long by 15 miles wide in the very heart of the Alaska Range. They adjoin the Alaska Railroad from McKinley Park station southward almost to Windy and are widely distributed along the McKinley Park Highway.

In the eastern part of the syncline, as far west as the East Fork of the Toklat River, the rocks are prevailingly dark gray or almost black, as, for example, on Sable Mountain north of Sable Pass on the McKinley Park Highway. Westward, however, around Polychrome Pass, the sandstone and conglomerate form conspicuous, light-brown, almost buff-colored, mountains. In their upper part the sediments are interbedded with volcanic rocks, including rhyolite and andesite flows and tuffs and flows of obsidian. Dark-brown andesite flows form Mount Fellows, across the river from McKinley Park Hotel. In the Polychrome Pass area, and farther west, beyond Camp Eielson, the volcanic rocks are colored brightly in shades of red, pink, purple, yellow, and white. Indeed, it was the brilliant coloring of the volcanic rocks that suggested the name Polychrome for the pass. A detached remnant of volcanic rocks forms the white cone of Sugar Mountain, 5 miles southeast of Healy, and Jumbo Dome, 10 miles northeast of Healy. The mountain-building forces that compressed the sediments and volcanic rocks to produce their present attitudes was the last great crustal movement to give the Alaska Range its basic synclinal structure, and the volcanic rocks are the youngest of the well-consolidated rocks of the Alaska Range.

The next younger rocks show that after mountain-building movements had folded and solidified the Cretaceous rocks just described, most of the Alaska Range was again reduced to low relief. Here and there, however, hills rose 1,000 feet above the general level, and it was around these that the next sediments accumulated, forming poorly consolidated coal-bearing rocks of Eocene age. These rocks, although not widespread, are tremendously important because of the immense reserves of coal they contain. The largest area of such rocks is the Nenana coal field in the northern foothills of the Alaska Range, where they extend as a disconnected band from the Toklat River eastward to the Wood River, but the thickest and largest deposits of coal are along Healy and Lignite creeks. Beds of coal can be seen clearly from the Alaska Railroad at Lignite, where they are thrown into a sharp uparch on the opposite bank of the Nenana River. They can also be seen from the train on the north bank of Healy Creek, where the coal mines at Suntrana are situated.

The coal-bearing beds are made up of chalky-white and pale-buff sandstone, brown and gray-green claystone, and coal. Alternations of light sandstone bands and black coals give a zebra-striped appearance to many of the cliffs and badlands; indeed the large outcrops on the banks of Lignite Creek are among the most brilliant rock exposures anywhere in the entire Alaska Range (pl. 13).

Overlying these beds are coarse, brown to red conglomerates known as Nenana gravel. Near Healy, this gravel accumulated to a thickness of more than 3,000 feet, and it is widespread along the north flank of the Alaska Range. It was laid down during the last major period of folding and faulting in the Alaska Range, that is, when the coal beds were being deformed. The Nenana gravel is, then, the detritus shed from the mountains that rose as a result of this deformation. In fact, by determining the sources of the boulders and pebbles in the gravel, it is possible to tell where the mountains were rising and the order in which they rose, and thus to reconstruct, even though imperfectly, the history of the uplift of the Alaska Range.

Both the Nenana gravel and the underlying coal-bearing beds are extremely soft and easily weathered; hence the areas they occupy are low-lying, commonly low passes and plains. No doubt they once covered a much larger part of Alaska than they do now, and have been largely removed by erosion. Many east-west valleys and low passes, otherwise inexplicable, may be accounted for by the former presence of Tertiary rocks downfolded into synclines along the sites of valleys and passes and then removed by erosion.

The youngest rocks of all are unconsolidated deposits derived from all the older rocks by weathering, creep, landslides, and other processes and transported and redeposited by rivers and glaciers. They are widespread throughout the Alaska Range, mantling most of the valleys within the range as well as the lowlands to the north and south. They provide a record of successive glaciations during Pleistocene and Recent times and reveal much of the history of the modeling of the landscape.

Among these young deposits are four types. First, there is the mantle of talus that covers much of the hillsides. In many places it creeps slowly downslope under the influence of frost action. Below each colored outcrop there is a streak of talus of the same color, the total effect being to give the mountains a streaming appearance as if talus were cascading down the mountainsides. Such streaming talus is beautifully displayed on the mountains of Birch Creek schist north of McKinley Park station and on the mountains of volcanic rock around Sable and Polychrome passes.

The second type of youthful deposit was laid down by glaciers. It includes the till and moraines built by glaciers as they pushed or carried debris from the high mountains and deposited it as they wasted away in the lowlands. Areas of glacial moraine are typically chaotic jumbles of small mounds and depressions, dotted with many lakes. The region traversed by the Richardson Highway near Donnelly Dome shows characteristic morainal topography, and the ridges along the highway north of the dome are terminal moraines marking the northern limit of the great Delta River Glacier during its last advance. The McKinley Park Highway for many miles east of Wonder Lake follows a huge lateral moraine of the Muldrow Glacier of Pleistocene time.

The third kind of youthful deposit includes terrace deposits and outwash. All rivers of the Alaska Range, whether glacial or not, deposited enormous loads of gravel in their beds during cold periods because of quickened frost-erosion and glacial action. When the glaciers retreated, however, the rivers eroded these deposits, leaving remnants along the banks as terraces or benches. Stream-deposited and stream-cut terraces formed in this way extend for miles along most of the principal rivers. Those along the Nenana River, which can be seen from the Alaska Railroad, are among the most complicated sets ever described.

The fourth and last type of young deposit was laid down by wind. Deposits of wind-blown sand and silt mantle most of the low terraces and hills along the north side of the Alaska Range, and dunes are present in some places. Study of these various unconsolidated deposits has demonstrated that glaciers accumulated in the mountains and advanced to the lowlands, only to melt and retreat, at least four and possibly more than six times within the past several hundred thousand years.

HOWARD A. POWERS

Alaska Peninsula–Aleutian Islands

The Alaska Peninsula and Aleutian Islands form one of the conspicuously arcuate lines of volcanoes that border the Pacific Ocean. The name Aleutian Range is applied to this 1,600-mile long, narrow belt of peaks reaching from Mount Spurr opposite Anchorage to the island of Attu, close to the continent of Asia. Nearly eighty volcanoes have been recognized within this belt; some have been partly destroyed by erosion, but fifty-eight of them have scarcely been modified from their original forms and have erupted lava flows or ash beds since the last major stage of glaciation. No less than forty-seven volcanoes are known to be steaming or have been reported as active since 1760.

The deeply eroded basement upon which these volcanoes rest is itself made up largely of volcanic rocks, but so old that the initial volcanic landforms have been destroyed.

Accompanying these early volcanic rocks, some of which are more than 50 million years old, are stratified sediments derived by their erosion. Both kinds of basement rocks are cut by dikes and irregular masses of coarsely

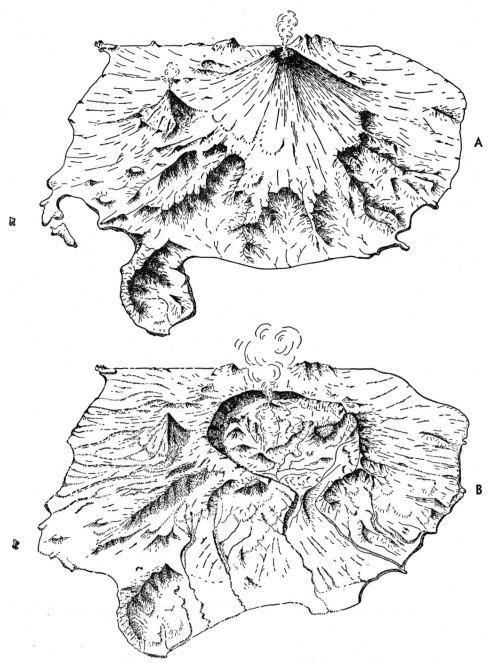

Figure 1. Evolution of Okmok caldera, Umnak Island. *A.* Ancestral Okmok volcano. *B.* Caldera formed by collapse of the top of Okmok volcano. Younger lava flows and cinder cones have partly filled the caldera. (Redrawn from Alaska Volcano Investigations Report No. 2, Pt. 3, Fig. 9, 1947.)

crystalline plutonic rocks, such as gabbro, diorite, and granite, which represent intrusions of molten material that failed to reach the surface, but cooled slowly underground. All the bedrocks and the intrusions that cut them were much broken by faults, elevated above sea level, and deeply carved by ocean waves, streams, and ice before the younger volcanoes began to cover them.

It must not be supposed from the abundance of active volcanoes that several eruptions can be seen during a brief visit. Much depends on what kind of activity the visitor hopes to see. If he is satisfied to see a plume of steam rising quietly from a summit crater or from a fissure on the flank of a cone, his chances are good, for "steamers" are scattered along the whole length of the Aleutian Range. The chances of seeing a small puff of ash and fume are also quite good, as may be judged from the list of active volcanoes in table 1, and from the known record of activity.

This record, moreover, is probably far from complete, certainly during the early years, because observers were few and visibility was often extremely poor. Table 1 also shows that ash-producing explosions are typical of most Aleutian volcanoes. Excellent and readily accessible examples of explosive volcanoes are Pavlof, Shishaldin, and Akutan. Weather permitting, the visitor will probably see at least puffs of fume, and perhaps small bursts of ash from any one of these three at almost any time. The first two are magnificent, symmetrical cones, like the famous Fujiyama of Japan and Mayon of the Philippines, formed by long-continued discharge of ash and occasional outflows of lava. Other symmetrical cones in the Aleutian Range are Vsevidof on western Umnak Island, Carlisle and Cleveland in the Islands of the Four Mountains, and Kanaga, Tanaga, and Gareloi on islands of the same names. The craters of all of these steam at intervals.

Akutan may once have been a symmetrical cone like Pavlof and Shishaldin, but its top has disappeared, leaving in its place a large caldera, within which renewed activity is now building a second symmetrical cone. Structures of this kind, in which younger cones grow within a large caldera, are common among Aleutian volcanoes, as may be seen in table 2. Indeed the "Buldir depression," a submarine basin recently discovered between Kiska and Buldir islands by the U.S. Coast and Geodetic Survey, has usurped the place formerly taken by the Valles caldera of New Mexico as the largest known caldera in the world. Its steep inner walls and relatively flat floor, and the presence within it of several conical seamounts, as well as its position along the Aleutian volcanic zone, leave no doubt that it is a caldera, even though it measures 27 by 13 miles across.

TABLE 1

Volcanoes of the Aleutian Range [1]

Name	Approximate height (in feet)	Geographic locality	Remarks on activity
Spurr	11,069	Aleutian Range	1953 ash eruption, 1954 ash eruption
Black	6,000	Aleutian Range	Probably no historic activity
Double	6,400	Aleutian Range	Probably no historic activity
Redoubt	11,200	Aleutian Range	1778 active,[2] 1819 smoke,[3] 1902 active, 1933 smoke
Iliamna	10,085	Aleutian Range	1768 smoke, 1786 smoke, 1867 ash eruption, 1876 smoke, 1933 smoke, 1947 smoke, 1952–1953 smoke
Augustine	3,970	Augustine Island	1812 active, 1883 ash eruption, 1935 lava eruption
Douglas	7,064	Alaska Peninsula	Steaming intermittent
Fourpeaked	6,903	Alaska Peninsula	Probably no historic activity
Unnamed	2,800	Alaska Peninsula	Probably no historic activity
Kukak	6,710	Alaska Peninsula	Probably no historic activity
Steller	6,900	Alaska Peninsula	Probably no historic activity
Denison	7,200	Alaska Peninsula	Probably no historic activity
Katmai	7,500	Alaska Peninsula	Ash eruption, steaming since
Trident	6,300	Alaska Peninsula	1912 steaming, 1953 lava eruption
Knife Peak	7,000	Alaska Peninsula	Probably no historic activity
Novarupta	2,700	Alaska Peninsula	1912 lava and ash eruption
Mageik	7,500	Alaska Peninsula	1912 ash eruption, 1927 ash eruption, 1929 active, 1936 ash eruption, 1946 active, 1953 ash eruption
Martin	7,250	Alaska Peninsula	Steaming intermittent since 1912
Peulik	5,000	Alaska Peninsula	1814 ash eruption, 1852 smoke
Chiginagak	6,700	Alaska Peninsula	1852 smoke, steaming intermittent
Aniakchak	4,420	Alaska Peninsula	1931 lava eruption, steaming
Purple	3,130	Alaska Peninsula	Probably no historic activity
Veniaminof	8,400	Alaska Peninsula	1830–1838 smoking, 1838 ash eruption, 1852 smoke, 1874 smoke, 1892 ash eruption, 1930 lava eruption, 1939 ash eruption, 1944 active
Kupreanof	5,000	Alaska Peninsula	Probably no historic activity
Dana	4,200	Alaska Peninsula	Probably no historic activity

[1] From "Volcanic Activity in the Aleutian Arc," by R. R. Coats, U.S. Geological Survey. Bull. 974-B, 1950, with some addition. Names of volcanoes arranged in geographic sequence from east to west.
[2] Active according to records, but type of activity not stated.
[3] Smoke is a word used in records; it refers to steam or steam-and-ash clouds.

TABLE 1—*continued*

Name	Approximate height (in feet)	Geographic locality	Remarks on activity
Pavlof Sister	7,000	Alaska Peninsula	1762–1786 active
Pavlof	8,900	Alaska Peninsula	1790 active, 1838 smoke, 1846 ash eruption, 1852 smoke, 1866 ash eruption, 1880 active, 1892 active, 1901 ash eruption, 1917 ash eruption, 1922–1924 ash eruption, 1929–1931 ash eruptions, 1936–1945 ash eruptions, 1948 ash eruption, 1950–1953 ash eruptions
Double Crater	4,300	Alaska Peninsula	Probably no historic activity
Hague	4,300	Alaska Peninsula	Steaming intermittent
Emmons	4,200	Alaska Peninsula	Probably no historic activity
Frosty	5,820	Alaska Peninsula	Probably no historic activity
Amak	1,682	Amak Island	Probably no historic activity
Roundtop	6,140	Unimak Island	1825 ash eruption, probably some eruptions reported for Isanotski should be credited to Roundtop
Isanotski	8,435	Unimak Island	1795 ash eruption, 1830 ash eruption, 1845 active (perhaps these are Roundtop eruptions)
Shishaldin	9,978	Unimak Island	1775–1778 active, 1790 smoke, 1824–1826 ash eruption, 1827–1830 ash eruption, 1838 ash eruption, 1842 ash eruption, 1865 smoke, 1880–1881 smoke, 1883 ash eruption, 1897 smoke, 1898 ash eruption, 1922 ash eruption, 1925 ash eruption, 1928–1929 ash eruption, 1946–1953 ash eruption, 1955 ash eruption
Fisher	3,590	Unimak Island	1826, perhaps ash eruption
Westdahl	5,035	Unimak Island	Probably no historic activity
Pogramni	7,500	Unimak Island	1795 ash eruption, 1796 lava flow, 1820 ash eruption, 1827–1830 ash eruption
Akun	4,244	Akun Island	Steaming intermittent
Akutan	4,244	Akutan Island	1790 smoke, 1828 smoke, 1838 active, 1848 ash eruption, 1852 active, 1865 active, 1867 smoke, 1883 ash eruption, 1887 lava eruption, 1892 smoke, 1896 active, 1907 ash eruption, 1908 lava eruption, 1911–1912 ash eruptions, 1927–1928 ash eruption, 1929 lava flow, 1931 ash eruption, 1946 ash eruption, 1948–1953 ash eruption

TABLE 1—*continued*

VOLCANOES OF THE ALEUTIAN RANGE

Name	Approximate height (in feet)	Geographic locality	Remarks on activity
Table Top	2,710	Unalaska Island	Probably no historic activity
Makushin	6,680	Unalaska Island	1768–1769 ash eruption, 1790 smoke, 1802 ash eruption, 1818 smoke, 1826 ash eruption, 1827–1838 smoke, 1845 smoke, 1865 active, 1867 smoke, 1883 ash eruption, 1907 active, 1912 active, 1926 ash eruption, 1938 ash eruption, 1951 ash eruption, 1952 smoke
Bogoslof	300	Bogoslof Island	1796 lava eruption, 1806 lava eruption, 1814 ash eruption, 1820 smoke, 1882 ash eruption, 1883 lava eruption, 1890–1891 explosions, 1906 lava eruption, 1907 lava eruption, 1909 lava eruption, 1910 explosions, 1913 smoke, 1926 ash eruption, 1926–1927 lava eruption, 1931 ash eruption, 1951 (?) ash eruption
Tulik	4,111	Umnak Island	Probably no historic activity
Okmok	3,519	Umnak Island	1817 ash eruption, 1824–1830 active, probably a lava flow, 1899 ash eruption, 1931 ash eruption, 1936 smoke, 1938 lava flow, 1945 lava flow, steaming since
Recheschnoi	6,510	Umnak Island	Probably no historic activity
Vsevidof	6,920	Umnak Island	1784 smoke, 1790 smoke, 1830 active, 1878 ash eruption, 1880 smoke, 1957 smoke
Kagamil	2,920	Umnak Island	1929 active, intermittent steaming
Tana	3,840	Chuginadak Island	Probably no historic activity
Cleveland	6,500	Chuginadak Island	1893 active, 1929 ash eruption, 1932 smoke, 1938 active, 1944 ash eruption, steaming intermittent
Uliaga	2,910	Uliaga Island	Probably no historic activity
Carlisle	6,200	Carlisle Island	1774 active, 1828 active, 1838 smoke
Herbert	4,235	Herbert Island	Probably no historic activity
Yunaska	3,119	Yunaska Island	1817 smoke, 1824 ash eruption, 1830 ash eruption, 1929 smoke, 1937 ash eruption
Chagulak	3,750	Chagulak Island	Probably no historic activity
Amukta	3,463	Amukta Island	1786–1791 active, 1876 smoke

TABLE 1—*continued*

Name	Approximate height (in feet)	Geographic locality	Remarks on activity
Seguam	3,440	Seguam Island	1827 smoke, 1891–1892 ash eruptions, 1902 ash eruption, 1927 smoke
Sarichef	1,000	Atka Island	1812 active, 1907 ash eruption
Kliuchef	2,800	Atka Island	Probably no historic activity
Korovin	3,852	Atka Island	1829–1830 smoke, 1844 smoke, 1951 smoke
Sergief	1,700	Atka Island	Probably no historic activity
Koniuji	1,113	Koniuji Island	1760 active, 1827–1828 smoke
Kasatochi	1,018	Kosatochi Island	1899 crater lake disappeared, and steam rose from crater
Great Sitkin	5,740	Great Sitkin Island	1760 smoke, 1784 smoke, 1792 ash eruption, 1829 smoke, 1904 smoke, 1933 ash eruption, 1945 lava eruption, 1949–1950 ash eruptions
Adagdak	1,900	Adak Island	Probably no historic activity
Moffett	3,900	Adak Island	Probably no historic activity
Kanaga	4,416	Kanaga Island	1786 ash eruption, 1790–1791 active, 1827 smoke, 1829 smoke, 1904 lava flows, intermittent steaming
Bobrof	2,400	Bobrof Island	No historic activity
Takawangha	4,600	Tanaga Island	No historic activity
Tanaga	6,972	Tanaga Island	1763–1770 active, 1791 smoke, 1829 smoke, 1914 lava flow, intermittent steaming
Gareloi	5,334	Gareloi Island	1760 smoke, 1790–1792 ash eruptions, 1828 smoke, 1873 active, 1922 ash eruption, 1927 smoke, 1929 lava flows, intermittent steaming
Sugar Loaf	2,500	Semisopochnoi Island	No historic activity
Cerberus	2,400	Semisopochnoi Island	1772 smoke, 1790–1792 smoke, 1830 smoke, 1873 active
Anvil Peak	3,867	Semisopochnoi Island	No historic activity
Little Sitkin	3,921	Little Sitkin Island	1776 active, 1828 smoke
Davidof-Kvostof	1,000	Davidof-Kvostof Island	No historic activity
Segula	3,799	Segula Island	Steaming intermittent
Kiska	3,996	Kiska Island	Steaming intermittent
Buldir	2,500	Buldir Island	No historic activity

TABLE 2

CALDERAS OF THE ALEUTIAN RANGE [1]

(Arranged in order of location from east to west)

Name	Geographic location	Approximate diameter (in miles)
Unnamed	Alaska Peninsula	1¾
Katmai	Alaska Peninsula	3 x 1¾
Aniakchak	Alaska Peninsula	5¾ x 5
Purple	Alaska Peninsula	1⅔
Veniaminof	Alaska Peninsula	5
Frosty	Alaska Peninsula	3⅓
Fisher	Unimak Island	7 x 9 (?)
Akutan	Akutan Island	1¼
Makushin	Unalaska Island	2 x 1½
Okmok	Umnak Island	7¼
Yunaska	Yunaska Island	1¾ x 1½
Kliuchef	Atka Island	2⅔
Great Sitkin	Great Sitkin Island	1½ x 1
Kanaton	Kanaga Island	2½
Takawangha	Tanaga Island	2
Tanaga	Tanaga Island	6⅔
Semisopochnoi	Semisopochnoi Island	4½ x 3⅔
Little Sitkin	Little Sitkin Island	2¾
Davidof	Davidof-Kvostof Island	1½
"Buldir Depression"	West of Kiska Island	27 x 13

[1] Modified from Coats, 1950.

Calderas, unlike craters, are not eruptive vents but are formed by the collapse of the summits of large cones, generally as the result of colossal explosive eruptions. The cones do not "blow off" their heads; on the contrary, their heads cave into the underlying reservoirs when these are rapidly drained by discharge of enormous volumes of ash and pumice. After such engulfments the volcanoes may die; far more commonly, however, activity is resumed after a period of quiescence so that new cones develop within the calderas. On Semisopochnoi, for instance, the large triple-cratered cone of Cerberus occupies more than half of the caldera floor, towering above the caldera walls and nearly obliterating them on one side. Kanaga volcano likewise towers above the rim of Kanaton caldera. On the other hand, as may be seen in figure 1, none of the nine cones in the Okmok caldera on Umnak Island overtops the walls. A spectacular lava flow issued from an intracaldera cone in 1945, and the crater is said to have been steaming constantly ever since. Similar flows have been seen at Akutan caldera in 1929, and at Aniakchak caldera in 1931. A steep-sided, bulbous mass of viscous lava that rose within the caldera of Great Sitkin in 1945 is still steaming, and in 1949 and 1950 explosions of black ash took place from a small crater associated with it.

The most spectacular of all Alaskan historic eruptions was certainly that which took place in 1912. This formed the Valley of Ten Thousand Smokes and the adjacent caldera of Katmai, features so impressive scenically and so informative to the scientist that they have been set aside, together with neighboring volcanoes, as a National Monument to be preserved in their natural state by the National Park Service. Before the 1912 eruptions, there were two long-inhabited villages in the area, namely, Katmai, not more than 20 miles from the volcano, on the Pacific Coast, and Savonoski, at the head of the Naknek Lakes, on the Bering Sea side of the peninsula. A trail connected the two villages, traversing the heart of the volcanic area. And although the natives of Savonoski reported in 1898 that one of the volcanoes smoked occasionally, they knew of no eruption; hence, the cataclysm of 1912 seems to have been the first major outbreak in the area in several hundred years.

A very general description of the terrane before the eruption was given by J. E. Spurr, a pioneer Alaskan geologist, who led a U.S. Geological Survey party across the peninsula by way of the Savonoski-Katmai trail in 1898. Southward from Savonoski, the trail followed a broad, deep valley, floored with stream and glacial debris. The valley walls consist of marine sedimentary rocks containing Jurassic fossils; these rocks, here and elsewhere in the Alaska Peninsula, had already been lifted above the sea before any of the Cenozoic volcanoes began to erupt.

The first inkling of the tremendous outbursts in 1912 was a series of earthquakes felt by the villagers on June 1. "American" Pete, the chief of Savonoski, became apprehensive for the safety of his hunting equipment, stored in a camp at Ukak, about 10 miles south of the village, along the trail toward Katmai Pass. At approximately one o'clock on June 6 came the first eruption, a thunderous explosion of pumice and rock fragments from the present site of Novarupta, near the head of the Valley of Ten Thousand Smokes. Observers on the steamer *Dora*, 55 miles to the east across Shelikof Strait, saw the mushroom cloud and reported mistakenly that it came from Mount Katmai. "American" Pete, who was near Ukak at the time, was fortunate, for the wind was blowing from the southwest and none of the hot ejecta fell on him. Had he stayed to watch the eruptions for only a few hours, he would never have escaped to tell his tale, for the next outburst took place with such rapidity and violence that all living things in the valley were destroyed.

The pearly-white pumice of the first eruption had hardly stopped cascading down the snow-covered mountainsides near Novarupta when from the same vent and from nearby fissures there issued a colossal volume of white-hot powdery ash. Within a few moments, no less than 2½ cubic miles of ash were expelled, and the incandescent mass, acting like a fiery hot liquid, swept down the valley with incredible swiftness. Trees on the valleysides above the glowing avalanches were snapped off and carbonized by the scorching, tornadic wind. More than 40 square miles of the valley floor were buried beneath the ash, in places to a depth of 700 feet. No sooner had the glowing avalanches come to rest than hot gases, mostly steam derived from buried rivers and feeding springs, began to rise to the surface through myriads of small holes and cracks. When Robert F. Griggs first saw the valley, four years later, in 1916, the sight of these myriads of steam plumes led him to name this the Valley of Ten Thousand Smokes, and even then some of the fumaroles were still so hot that they ignited wood thrust into them.

At or about the same time as the glowing avalanches were discharged from Novarupta and adjacent fissures at the head of the valley, the entire top of Mount Katmai volcano, which lies 6 miles to the east, collapsed, leaving in place of its pointed peak a chasm almost 3 miles long and 2 miles wide. None can doubt that somewhere at depth the lava conduits under Katmai and Novarupta are connected, for although almost all of the ash and pumice issued from Novarupta, it was the top of Katmai that was engulfed.

A clue to the explanation of this puzzle is afforded by study of the kinds of material ejected by the two volcanoes. The first ejecta from Novarupta were composed of snow-white rhyolite pumice; then the ejecta changed suddenly to black-and-white streaked pumice composed partly of rhyolite and partly of andesite. Then followed brown pumice, apparently a homogeneous mixture of rhyolite and andesite, and finally white rhyolite lava issued sluggishly to build a dome within the crater. Mount Katmai may have discharged a little ash while Novarupta was active, but its main eruption certainly occurred after the mountaintop had collapsed to form the present caldera. Andesite, almost identical in composition with the dark streaks in the Novarupta pumice, was then erupted on the caldera floor, partly as lava and partly as cinders, forming a small cone that now lies submerged beneath hundreds of feet of beautiful, turquoise-blue water (see pl. 15).

The latest explanation of the great eruptions of 1912, which differs radically from earlier explanations, is therefore as follows: A column of molten andesite, which had been lying quietly in the conduit beneath Mount Katmai suddenly found access through newly created fissures to the erupting column of rhyolite beneath Novarupta, 6 miles away. Almost as rapidly as the two lavas mingled, they frothed upward and were erupted as hybrid pumice, and this chilling quickly, preserved the stages of mixing as light and dark streaks. And while the molten andesite drained from the conduit under Katmai to be expelled at Novarupta, nearly 5,000 feet lower, the unsupported top of the mountain collapsed into the void. Then, as activity subsided at Novarupta and its vent became tightly sealed by a plug of viscous rhyolite, molten andesite again rose in the conduit of Katmai, forcing its way through the mass of debris from the former summit to expand its waning energies in a feeble, dying gasp, building a small cone on the caldera floor.

In all, more than 7 cubic miles of pumice and broken rock were hurled into the atmosphere and stratosphere during these 1912 eruptions, and some of the ejecta were carried by winds to all parts of the northern hemisphere. And this vast mass of ejecta escaped in the almost incredibly short space of sixty hours! The total volume of debris was almost equal to that discharged during the greatest of all historic eruptions, that of Tamboro, in the East Indies, in 1815. But whereas 92,000 people lost their lives during the outbreak of Tamboro, not a single life was lost at Katmai.[1]

The adjacent Martin, Mageik, and Trident volcanoes began to steam while Katmai was active, and Mageik erupted explosively for five days late in August, 1927, at which time Captain Harry W. Crosby of the *Salmon King* collected pumice from the deck of his ship sailing 50 miles offshore. Nine years later, on July 4, 1936, Mageik again discharged showers of ash, and still again in 1946.

Trident burst into activity on February 15, 1953. The initial outbreak sent a column of "smoke" 30,000 feet into the air. The dispatcher for the Northern Consolidated Airlines at King Salmon, 75 miles away, and observers on a Navy plane flying about 50 miles away described it as a mushroom-shaped cloud "resembling the explosion of an atomic bomb." Fog and fume prevented ground observations for three days, but many explosion clouds were seen above the fog blanket during the next two days, ap-

[1] The foregoing account of the 1912 eruptions, including the new interpretation of what took place, was written by Professor Garniss Curtis, University of California, Berkeley, on the basis of field studies made in 1953 and 1954.

parently coming from two different sources, perhaps from Mageik or Martin as well as from Trident. On February 18, the weather cleared enough to disclose a thick, blocky lava flow issuing from a new dome at about 3,600 feet altitude on the southwest slope of the southwest peak of Trident, probably near where steam had been observed in June, 1951 (see pl. 17). Progress of the activity was carefully watched by Navy air patrols carrying observers from the Geological Survey. By March 11, the lava flow was nearly a mile long, a fifth of a mile wide, and from 200 to 600 feet thick.

The chances of seeing an active flow during a visit to the Aleutian Range are not good. Indeed only thirteen volcanoes are known to have erupted either flows or viscous domes of lava during the last two centuries. Table 3 lists the dates culled from records and confirmed by field examination. From this field check, it has been found that some of the recorded observations, such as ". . . a sheet of lava poured down the side of the volcano . . . ," actually referred to particularly vigorous falls of hot ash and cinders that looked from a distance like torrents of flowing lava. Extremely fresh lavas, not witnessed while moving but probably erupted during historic time, have been found on Segula, Little Sitkin, Semisopochnoi, Vsevidof, and Mount Hague.

TABLE 3

RECORD OF HISTORIC LAVA FLOWS

Date	Volcano	Nature of extrusion
1796	Bogoslof	Lava dome
1796	Pogromni	Lava flow
1824–1830	Okmok	Lava flow
1883	Bogoslof	Lava dome
1887(?)	Akutan	Lava flow
1904	Kanaga	Several lava flows
1906–1907	Bogoslof	Lava domes
1908	Akutan	Lava flow
1909	Bogoslof	Lava dome
1912	Novarupta	Lava dome
1914	Tanaga	Lava flow
1927	Bogoslof	Lava dome
1929	Gareloi	Several lava flows
1929	Akutan	Lava flow
1930	Veniaminof	Lava dome
1931	Aniakchak	Lava flow
1931(?)	Okmok	Lava flow (perhaps 1938)
1935	Augustine	Lava flow
1938(?)	Okmok	Lava flow
1945	Great Sitkin	Lava dome
1945	Okmok	Lava flow
1953	Trident	Lava dome and flow

Table 3 shows that the Bering Sea volcano Bogoslof has extruded lava more often within historic time than any other Aleutian volcano. When first discovered by Russian navigators in 1768, the island of Bogoslof consisted only of a small pinnacle, called Sail Rock or Ship Rock because of the resemblance of its profile to that of a sailing vessel.

In May, 1796, an eruption enlarged the island of Bogoslof. A résumé of Russian accounts of this eruption, quoted from *Alaska and Its Resources*, by W. H. Dall, published in 1870, is as follows:

> On the first of May (1796), according to Baranoff, a storm arose near Umnak, and continued for several days. It was very dark all this time, and low noises resembling thunder were continually heard. On the third day the sky became clear very early, and a flame was seen arising from the sea between Unalaska and Umnak. North of the latter smoke was observed for 10 days. At the end of this time, from Unalaska a round white mass was seen rising from the sea. During the night fire arose in the same locality, so that objects 10 miles off were distinctly visible. An earthquake shook Unalaska, and was accompanied by fearful noises. Rocks were thrown from the new volcano as far as Umnak. With sunrise the noises ceased, the fire diminished, and the new island was seen in the form of a black cone. It was named after St. John the Theologian (Joanna Bogoslova). A month later it was considerably higher, and emitted flames constantly. It continued to rise, but steam and smoke took the place of fire. Four years after no smoke was seen, and in 1804 the island was visited by hunters. They found the sea warm around it, and the soil in many places too hot to walk on. It was said to be 2½ miles around and 350 feet high. The soil emitted an odor of bitumen. In 1806 lava flowed from the summit into the sea on the north side. Fissures appeared, lined with crystals of sulphur. Veniaminof says that it ceased to enlarge in 1823, when it was of a pyramidal form and about 1,500 feet high. There are many strong currents about it, and a reef extends from a rock west of it to Umnak.

Bogoslof apparently remained quiet until 1882, when residents of Unalaska, 60 miles to the east, noticed steam rising from the ocean somewhat north of Ship Rock. A year later, on October 20, 1883, a violent eruption showered ash on the village. Another dome of lava was thrust above water shortly thereafter, forming an island to the north of Ship Rock. The three islands were now connected by bars of volcanic debris and boulder beaches. The new island, called both New Bogoslof and Grewingk, had a craggy profile, with pinnacles rising 500 feet above the sea. Bogoslof had been greatly reduced in size so that its three main crags were lower than the new island. Sketches show that Ship Rock still existed in 1887, but violent explosions must have taken place during the next few years, because pictures taken in 1891 no longer show it. Moreover, an open water channel then separated Old Bogoslof from Grewingk, and the craggy profile of Grewingk had been changed to a flat-topped mesa about 300 feet high, capped by a layer of bedded volcanic debris.

In 1906, another extrusion of viscous lava rose from the sea about halfway between Old Bogoslof and Grewingk. This new island, called Metcalf Cone, had on its top a broken spine like the famous spine that rose on top of the dome of Mount Pelée in the West Indies in 1902. The south half of Metcalf Cone was demolished by an explosion in 1907, and another dome of lava rose in the breach to form a new island connecting it with Old Bogoslof. This dome was called McCulloch Peak. Its life was brief, for it disappeared during a violent explosion on September 1, 1907, only days after members of an expedition from the Massachusetts Institute of Technology had sailed from Bogoslof. A thick mantle of debris was left on the remaining islands, and a quarter of an inch of ash fell on the village of Unalaska.

In 1909, another new island, Tahoma Peak, rose in the bay formed by the destruction of McCulloch Peak, and on September 18, and 19, 1910, explosions blasted a crater in its top. By 1922, explosions and marine erosion had removed all traces of both Metcalf Cone and Tahoma Peak, and Fire Island, the name given by the Coast Guard to Grewingk, had been reduced by erosion to a small "table-topped" islet, apparently not much larger than the original Ship Rock. Meanwhile, Castle Rock, the new name for the remnant of Old Bogoslof, had been reduced to two rocky horns with sand and gravel heaps piled against them. A wide channel of open water separated Fire Island from Castle Rock, where previously had existed in turn, Ship Rock, Metcalf Cone, McCulloch Peak, and Tahoma Peak.

Submarine explosions between the island remnants during 1926 preceded the rise of yet another steep-sided mass of viscous lava during the winter of 1926–27. A ring of explosion debris, 10 feet above high tides, surrounded the new dome and again joined Fire Island and Castle Rock. In July, 1927, the dome was almost circular in plan, about 200 feet high and 1,000 feet across, and was surrounded by a shallow lagoon of warm water.

An explosion was seen at Bogoslof on October 31, 1931, and floating pumice was observed in the water south of the island. In 1935, when the island was mapped by the Coast and Geodetic Survey, an open water channel again separated Fire Island from the 1927 dome, and Castle Rock. In the summer of 1947, when F. M. Byers, Jr., of the Geological Survey, visited Bogoslof, the islands had been appreciably reduced in size by wave erosion. Finally, on September 21, 1951, a coastwise vessel ran through "muddy water" for about 2 miles near Bogoslof. This disturbance seems to have been caused by a submarine explosion. Presumably other domical masses of viscous lava will rise at Bogoslof and these will be partly or wholly demolished by explosions and by wave attack, for this, as the foregoing record shows, has been the oft-repeated story of Bogoslof since records were first kept in 1796.

It should be noted in conclusion that the lavas and explosive materials produced by the Alaskan-Aleutian volcanoes vary widely in chemical composition. Some of the lavas, such as olivine basalts, are relatively rich in iron, lime, and magnesia, and poor in silica; others, such as rhyolites, are rich in silica, soda, and potash; but most of the lavas are andesites of intermediate composition. Taken together, they resemble the products of coeval volcanoes in the Cascade Range of the western states, in the East Indies, New Zealand, Japan, and the Andes of South America. Thus, in their arcuate alignment, in their shapes and behavior, and in the composition of their products the volcanoes of the Aleutian Range resemble those of other island festoons that border the Pacific Ocean. In one respect, however, they are unique; throughout most of their length they lie between the deep basins of the Bering Sea and the Pacific Ocean rather than along the edge of a continent. For this reason, the geophysicist and geologist alike find the Aleutian Range of special interest.

ROBERT F. BLACK

Lowlands and Plains of Interior and Western Alaska

The lowlands and plains of interior and western Alaska, though widely scattered, are typified by similar topography and a veneer of Quaternary sediments. They extend intermittently from the Bering Strait almost to the Canadian border, and from the Brooks Range on the north to the Alaska Range on the south. Together with their included highlands, they comprise all the area between the Brooks and Alaska ranges with the exception of the Seward Peninsula, the largest single lowland lying adjacent to the Alaska Range for almost its entire length.

In places, the lowlands and plains follow parts of major stream valleys, but elsewhere their trends show no systematic relationship to drainage lines. Some lowlands resemble slightly undulating plains; others are dotted with low hills, and still others are exceptionally wide flood plains and river deltas. Most of them lie within a few hundred feet of sea level; few rise as much as a thousand feet above the sea except near the highlands.

Only in local areas are the lowlands and plains free from a mantle of Quaternary deposits. Because they lie between highlands and mountains

76

that were glaciated during the last million years, they are for the most part deeply buried by the products of glacial and stream erosion. In this respect they are somewhat analogous to the valleys of the Basin and Range province of the western United States where each basin is filled with the products of erosion until it is drained into an adjacent basin on the persistent march of the streams to the sea. But because precipitation is greater in Alaska than in the Basin and Range province, drainage is connected from one basin to the next, and isolated basins having only interior drainage cannot develop.

The lowland deposits are of many kinds, including unconsolidated clay, silt, sand, and gravel. Not all the lowlands were buried completely by ice during the Pleistocene period, but many were. Glaciers advanced into them many times, and retreated during intervals when the climate was as warm, if not warmer than it is today. Consequently, materials formed by successive glaciations and by interglacial weathering and erosion are superimposed and also interfinger laterally. Coarse detritus is generally concentrated closer to the mountains than is the finer debris, but all of it was transported to its present position by water, ice, wind, and mass-wasting processes or by combinations of these processes.

Part of the long record before the last million years is recorded in consolidated rocks that protrude through the cover of Quaternary sediments. Even though most of the isolated mountains within the lowland province no longer foster glaciers they were formed early enough to be glaciated. Rocks of the Proterozoic era, more than 520 million years old, are to be seen here and there. These, and other rocks of Paleozoic age, are schists and gneisses, highly metamorphosed rocks derived chiefly from sediments and lavas. Thoroughly altered limestones are present among them, but micaceous types predominate.

Most of the rocks of the next younger era—the Mesozoic—were originally silt, sand, and gravel, and they are generally less altered than the earlier rocks, though much better consolidated than the younger deposits. Tertiary rocks were formerly widespread, but because of their poor consolidation they were easily eroded when the region emerged from the sea. Some of them are marine in origin but others were laid down on land, some of these being stream deposits that contain placer gold and tin.

The sea withdrew from interior Alaska only a million years ago, at the beginning of glacial time; indeed but for the filling of Quaternary sediments most of the lowlands would still be inland arms of the ocean, flooded to depths of several hundred feet. This last million years, though representing less than one two-thousandth part of the entire geological record, is the most interesting and best known interval in the history of the lowlands. It was an interval marked by many glacial advances and retreats, by mountain building, by rapid changes of flora in response to climatic fluctuations, by evolution of many new forms of life, and by extinction of such bizarre animals as the hairy mammoth, saber-toothed tiger, and wooly rhinoceros, remains of which have been preserved in nature's deep-freeze—permafrost.

Permafrost, or perennially frozen ground, is present in all the lowlands in spite of wide differences of climate. The temperature of the ground at a depth of about 50 to 100 feet in areas of permafrost and perhaps 30 to 60 feet in frost-free areas is within a few degrees of the mean annual air temperature. Permafrost, therefore, can be expected in favorable materials such as fine-grained, poorly drained silts, clays, and very fine sands at about the 32° F. isotherm. The factors controlling its formation are those controlling heat exchange between the earth and the atmosphere. For example, permafrost is present and still forming in the Bristol Bay area even though the average annual air temperature is about 34° F., but it is disappearing from some of the inland areas with average annual air temperatures of 26° to 28° F. This apparent discrepancy can be attributed to cloudiness during summer around Bristol Bay and to the general sunny summer weather in the inland areas, for clouds prevent the direct heat of the sun from being absorbed by the earth.

During glacial times, because the climate was generally colder than it is now, permafrost was widely developed. Some of it may have formed as long as a million years ago, but whether or not such permafrost could have survived the warm interglacial periods is conjectural. Most of the present permafrost certainly dates back only to the last major advance of the ice, some tens of thousands of years ago. Abundant bones and other remains of Pleistocene mammals are preserved within it, along with many forms of life that do not now exist in Alaska. In Siberia permafrost has preserved mammoths and mastodons so completely that their flesh has been eaten by men and dogs. In the Alaska "mucks" fine clayey silts with much organic matter and a fetid odor, hair, sinew, skin, and other soft parts are preserved, but little flesh remains.

Permafrost is present in most of the placer mines of Alaska, and often it determines whether or not mines can be operated economically. Moreover permafrost, along with the effects of seasonal freeze and thaw, is one of the most important factors affecting engineering projects in unconsolidated materials. Only an exceptional Alaskan is unaware of its presence because it influences his ground-water supply, his home, the roads he travels, the airfields from which he flies, and the fields he plows. Large masses of ice may still be seen in some of the placer mines, and widespread surface effects of permafrost, such as cave-in or thaw lakes, polygonal ground, pingos and other mounds, are obvious in many places.

The visitor who drives to Alaska from the States first crosses the interior lowlands shortly after passing the Canadian-Alaskan boundary. The road winds along the north side of a flat, 60 miles long and 20 to 30 miles wide, dotted with myriads of lakes and swamps. It traverses bedrock locally; elsewhere it crosses sand dunes and deltaic deposits. During the last major glaciation this huge flat was occupied by a lake that drained southeastward into Canada. At one stage the lake was several hundreds of feet deep, and some of its near-shore and deltaic deposits may still be seen in steep tributary gullies that drain into the upper Tanana River from the highlands to the north.

Shortly after the lake disappeared, winds whipped the bottom deposits into large sand dunes. These are now vegetated, especially by aspen trees which require several feet of well-drained soil for their roots. The areas between the dunes are low and swampy, and although they are also vegetated their flora is different. Permafrost here lies within a foot or two of the surface, the black spruce is the only tree that can withstand the shallow, cold, poorly drained soil and acid conditions. In places only shrubs, sedges, and a few other vascular plants and mosses grow.

Cave-in or thaw lakes are common, and these enlarge by thaw of ice in the permafrost and consequent destruction of the marginal forests. Meandering streams and sloughs from the Chisana (pronounced Shūshāna) and Nabesna rivers, tributaries of the Tanana, are bordered by heavily vegetated natural levees that provide a home for moose, spruce grouse, muskrat, mink, otter, and other swamp inhabitants.

The Northway airport, which was built as an emergency field during World War II for the ferrying of aircraft to Russia, was constructed partly on sand dunes and partly on filled-in sloughs and interslough areas with much permafrost. Great difficulty and expense were therefore involved in maintenance because the runway and buildings settled irregularly during thaw once the natural thermal regime had been disturbed. A layer of white ash, 2 to 6 inches thick, was spread over the entire area only a few hundred years ago from an unknown volcano in the St. Elias Mountains.

The Tok flat lies to the west and south of the Alaska Highway bridge over the Tanana River. It is much smaller than the Northway flat, and is hardly more than an enlargement of the Tanana Valley, which the Tok River has alluviated. To the northwest of Tanacross are low hills with typical kettle lakes in moraines deposited by former glaciers of the Alaska Range to the south. About 150 miles from the Canadian border, the Alaska Highway enters the Delta flat. This consists of the outwash plain and moraines of glaciers formerly occupying the Delta River Valley. The moraines are low and inconspicuous where crossed by the Alaska Highway, and so are the accompanying sand dunes. The Alaska Highway and the Richardson Highway cross the Tanana River where it flows in a deep narrow channel that seldom freezes. From there to Fairbanks the combined highways traverse several hilly belts separated by flats similar to those already described. South of the Tanana River lies a large flat penetrated only by hunters and trappers.

The Tanana River almost everywhere along the route of the Alaska Highway lies on the north side of the valley and in many places it impinges against the highlands or cuts through them. The Alaska Range, having much higher precipitation, supplies many more tributaries than does the lower highland to the north. Furthermore, most of the tributaries from the Alaska Range are fed by glaciers and therefore carry much sediment; for that reason the apron of debris deposited by them has shoved the Tanana River northward.

Fairbanks is the center of an active placer gold mining area. In the placers at Ester, on the border between the highlands and lowlands, one may watch miners stripping the overburden of silt, muck, and gravel to permit the operation of dredges in the "pay dirt," and it comes as a surprise to see them unearth large masses of clear ice from the enclosing black muck when the daily temperature may be over 90° F. (see pl. 19). With luck, one may also catch a glimpse of bones, tree stumps, and other remains being exposed by the hydraulic giants; if not, they can be examined at the museum of the University of Alaska.

The age of the gravel in the beds of the buried stream valleys is late Pliocene or early Pleistocene. In many places the gravel is covered by several mucks, each representing a different climate and time of deposition. Much of the muck resulted from slump and flow of silt initially laid down on hilltops by winds that blew the fine constituents from glacial bars and flats. Occasionally whole forests, beaver ponds and dams, and even tunnels and holes of shrews and voles were covered and perennially frozen beneath such flows and slides. Hereabouts also bones of extinct bison, mammoth, mastodon, giant elk, Pleistocene moose and horse, and other animals have been unearthed.

The lowlands southwest of Fairbanks and elsewhere in interior Alaska are similar to those just discussed. Gravels lie closest to the mountains and fine materials farther out, a condition reflected in the drainage, permafrost, and vegetation. Where drainage is good, vegetation is luxurious, but where permafrost comes close to the surface the trees become stunted and finally die, to be replaced by shrubs, sedges, grasses, and other vascular plants and mosses. Streams that originate in the flats are sluggish and brown from organic material, and cave-in lakes are plentiful. Still visible are sand dunes derived from the outwash plains of former glaciers whose telltale moraines are only faintly discernible.

Polygonal patterns appear on the surface where the climate is more severe. These may be caused by seasonal frost, by relics of ice-wedge polygons, or by growth of ice wedges in permafrost. Some low mounds are formed by heaving of the surface through the force of water trapped between the seasonally freezing zone and permafrost, or through refreezing of drained lakes. Successive belts of vegetation, commonly of large poplars, white spruce, and shrub tundra, border the meandering rivers. These reflect the progressively closer approach of the permafrost to the surface in the bordering regions and its absence beneath the flood plains. Adverse climatic conditions and high permafrost table have prevented the growth of trees on the Yukon-Kuskokwim delta; in that region sloughs, lakes, and marshes provide ideal nesting grounds for wildfowl.

JOSEPH M. HOARE

Interior Highlands of Western Alaska

The interior highlands of western Alaska consist of two semiparallel, irregular belts that trend from southwest Alaska into west-central Alaska. The western belt encircles Norton Sound, stretching 380 miles from the Yukon-Kuskokwim delta to the lowlands near the head of the Kobuk River. Its width varies from 35 to 110 miles. The eastern belt, about 550 miles in length and from 35 to 150 miles in width, lies athwart the Kuskokwim River, extending northeastward from Bristol Bay to the broad lowlands of the Yukon and Tanana rivers.

These two highland areas are so similar geologically that they may be considered as a single unit superficially split by the Yukon-Innoko and Kuskokwim rivers. They are referred to for convenience as the Norton Sound highlands and Kuskokwim highlands. The latter are bounded on the east by the broad lowland of the Tanana, upper Kuskokwim, and Nushagak rivers and their many tributaries. The Norton Sound highlands are separated from the Seward Peninsula by a line running from the head of Norton Bay to the head of Kotzebue Sound. West of this line, in the

Seward Peninsula, most of the rocks are older, more massive, and more complexly deformed, and most of the mountains are higher and more rugged than those to the east, in the Norton Sound highlands.

The Norton Sound highlands and the northern part of the Kuskokwim highlands, commonly known as the Kuskokwim Mountains, are low, rolling mountains that extend with the monotonous regularity of ocean waves from one horizon to the other. The ridge crests are barren of all vegetation except for a few lichens and mosses which give them a light-gray color. Their roundness results from an extensive mantle of frost-ruptured bedrock several feet deep, developed in relatively weak graywackes and shales of Cretaceous age that constitute all but the south end of the Norton Sound highlands and most of the Kuskokwim highlands. Solifluction, rather than running water, moves the ruptured rocks downslope. This process, typical of arctic and subarctic regions involves the heave and thrust of frost on large volumes of loose material which then moves downhill en masse. The characteristic hillside forms that result are lobate waves which look from a distance as if they had been produced by flow of an extremely viscous substance like tar. Such forms may develop to a limited degree on many kinds of rocks, but they reach their fullest expression only where the rock detritus is fairly fine.

Most of the rounded ridge-crests trend northeastward, parallel to the geologic structures and drainage pattern, and because they vary little in height, ranging generally between 1,500 and 2,000 feet above sea level, it is believed that they developed by uplift and mature dissection of an old and flatter erosion surface that had evolved at a much lower elevation.

Numerous isolated, nearly circular groups of mountains 8 to 15 miles in diameter rise above the general level of the accordant ridges. These were monadnocks, that is, highlands that were never reduced to the common level of the old erosion surface because of their greater resistance to denudation. They are sharp peaks and ridges, between 4,000 and 5,000 feet high, carved in hornfelses and granitic rocks of Tertiary or late Cretaceous age. Examples include the Beaver and the Sunshine Mountains near McGrath, the Horn and the Russian Mountains north of the Kuskokwim River between Aniak and Crooked Creek, and the Chuilnuk, the Kiokluk, and the Taylor Mountains south of the Kuskokwim River. Their sharpness contrasts strongly with the rounded, rolling terrane that surrounds them, the difference being due partly to the massive, resistant character of the rocks and partly to the fact that only the higher areas were glaciated.

Cirques at the heads of broad and deep, U-shaped valleys floored with morainic debris give unmistakable evidence of relatively recent glaciation. Such signs of ice sculpture and deposition are generally found only on the north and west sides of these isolated groups of peaks, because with few exceptions it was only on these shaded sides that enough snow and ice accumulated to form glaciers.

The southern third of the Kuskokwim highlands consists of relatively higher and more rugged mountains, most of which were covered by ice during the Pleistocene period. Several small glaciers still survive among the jagged peaks and ridges in the northeast part. On recent maps the region has been separated arbitrarily into four parts. The Tikchik Mountains include the area drained mainly by the Tikchik and Nuyakuk rivers on the east and by the extreme headwaters of the Togiak River on the south. The Wood River Mountains, which lie south of the Tikchik Mountains and east of the Togiak River, are drained mainly by the Wood River and its many tributaries and by smaller streams, such as the Kulukak River, which also empty into Bristol Bay. The Kilbuck Mountains lie west of the Tikchik Mountains and south of the Kuskokwim Mountains, and their southern boundary is marked approximately by the headwaters of the Kanektok River. The large ill-defined mountainous area between the Togiak and Kanektok rivers is referred to as the Ahklune Mountains; these are drained by the Kanektok, Goodnews, Osviak, Togiak, and several smaller rivers.

All four of the above mountain groups are typified by high, sharp ridges or series of ridges separated by broad, flat, alluviated valleys. Toward the southwest, the ridges average only 1,000 to 2,000 feet in elevation and have rounded contours, but in the opposite direction they become progressively rougher and higher until they range from 3,000 to 4,000 feet in height, a few peaks, such as Mount Oratio and Mount Waskey, reaching altitudes of more than 5,000 feet. The height and sharpness of the peaks and ridges result from intense glacial sculpture of massive rocks of late Paleozoic and early Mesozoic age.

Except for the Brooks and Alaska ranges, the southern end of the Kuskokwim highlands is the largest glaciated area in interior Alaska. Enough snow and ice accumulated on the higher peaks during Pleistocene time to form glaciers, and the largest of these pushed down valleys radiating from the Tikchik Mountains. At least two advances took place, the earlier being by far the more extensive. At that time, the Goodnews and Togiak glaciers stretched from the Tikchik Mountains to the sea, whereas during the latest advance the Goodnews Glacier pushed only to a point a few miles west of

Goodnews Lake, and the Togiak Glacier pushed only a few miles south of Togiak Lake. Now only small glaciers and ice fields remain in the heads of the highest valleys, and even these are shrinking.

In all of the western interior highlands there are few more scenic glacial features than the deep lakes on the eastern edge of the Tikchik and the Wood River Mountains. Thirteen of the larger lakes, some of which are 35 miles long and 5 to 6 miles wide, are shown on most small-scale maps of Alaska. They lie between lofty serrate ridges in deep glacial troughs the bottoms of which have been scoured by ice to depths far below sea level. Long stretches of sand and gravel beaches form their eastern shores, whereas vertical cliffs and rocky promontories interspersed with small gravelly bays are typical of their western ends. Many of the lakes are connected by short, swift streams navigable by small boats.

Mining has been the main source of revenue, either directly or indirectly, for practically all the nonnative inhabitants of the western interior highlands since early in the present century. The first gold prospectors and miners were among the disappointed thousands who stampeded to the vicinity of Nome and then wandered elsewhere to try their luck; others worked their way inland after first landing at St. Michael.

Placer gold was found in paying quantities, and by 1911, it was being mined from many streams throughout the highlands. All of it was found near granitic and rhyolitic rocks, for these contain the lode gold from which the placer deposits were derived. Most of the mines are in unglaciated parts of the highlands, away from the disturbing action of glacial ice and torrential glacial streams. Placer gold was found at an early date near Christmas Mountain northeast of Norton Bay, and near Marshall on the Yukon River, and nearby placer mines are still the main source of revenue for the town of Marshall. Most of the placer gold of western interior Alaska has come, however, from the Kuskokwim highlands, the reason being that the intrusive rocks with which the gold is associated are far more abundant there.

The largest influx of prospectors and miners took place between 1911 and 1915, and during that brief period the population of the region was many times greater than it has ever been since. Discovery of rich deposits of placer gold on Flat Creek near Iditarod about 1914 caused the biggest stampede. For a short time during the summer of 1914, about 5,000 gold-hungry men lived in and near Iditarod, and from that time until the early 1940's the town of Flat was one of the largest placer gold camps in Alaska. Most of the mines have since been exhausted and now Iditarod is a ghost town without a single permanent inhabitant. On the river banks near town lie rotting hulks of small barges and stern-wheel paddle steamers that once brought freight and passengers up the tortuous Innoko and Iditarod rivers from Holy Cross on the Yukon.

Many disappointed men rushed to Iditarod, then drifted eastward and southward, prospecting as they went; probably no tributary of the Kuskokwim River was overlooked by them in at least a cursory search for the yellow metal. Small amounts of gold were found in many streams, but seldom was enough discovered to make mining profitable. The towns and mining camps of Ruby, Long, Poorman, McGrath, Tokatna, Ophir, Aniak, Nyac, and Bethel obtain much or all of their revenue from nearby gold mines. Bethel and McGrath, the two largest towns on the Kuskokwim River, lie respectively at the beginning and end of steamboat navigation, and though not mining towns they owe much of their livelihood to mining. All heavy supplies and equipment come as far as Bethel on ocean vessels, and there they are transshipped to barges and pushed up river by one or more wood-burning stern-wheelers as far as McGrath, the immediate source of supply for adjacent mining camps. Living conditions in these camps vary from crude to very comfortable indeed.

The time-honored tools of the gold miner—the pick and shovel, wheelbarrow, horse-drawn scraper, rocker, and long tom—have been replaced by modern machinery—the snorting bulldozer tractor, swaying dragline, and dredge with its endless string of buckets gnawing through the placer deposits.

Some of those who drifted from the Iditarod area worked their way south to Bristol Bay; others entered the southern end of the Kuskokwim highlands by way of Bristol Bay. They found gold in paying quantities on several creeks north and east of Goodnews Bay, and mining has continued intermittently in that area since about 1916. Gold was also found a few miles south of Goodnews Bay on the east side of a broad, round eminence known as Red Mountain, composed almost entirely of dunite and peridotite, heavy, dark intrusive rocks that weather red and so give the place its name.

The early miners found a heavy, black, nonmagnetic mineral among their gold concentrates, and for several years they separated it laboriously from the gold and threw it away. After some time, however, the annoying black sand was identified as platinum, a metal far more valuable than gold. Its source was undoubtedly Red Mountain, for it is with rocks such as dunite and peridotite, composed mainly or largely of the mineral olivine, that platinum is generally associated. The accompanying gold, however, was probably derived from adjacent areas of granitic rocks.

Large-scale mining of platinum did not begin until 1936, for not until then did any single group control enough of the deposit to warrant purchase of the expensive equipment needed for successful operations. Now the platinum-bearing gravels are being worked with a large electric dredge, and not only is the deposit the largest single domestic source of platinum, but the camp is among the largest and most comfortable in Alaska.

Quicksilver and scheelite (tungsten ore) are the only other minerals that have been mined in this part of Alaska. Scheelite was found, in 1947, on a small tributary of the Holitna River by a prospector who subsequently mined and sold a few thousand dollars worth of it. Quicksilver in the form of cinnabar has been found in placer concentrates at many places, and vein deposits of sufficient size to warrant mining have been found at five localities. Two of these discoveries were made by disappointed prospectors who drifted away from the Iditarod area. One deposit lies about 40 miles southwest of Flat, near what is now known as DeCourcy Mountain; the other is on the Kuskokwim River about 8 miles below the village of Sleetmute. Small mines had been opened at both places by 1914, and a small amount of "quick" had been produced by crude, makeshift retorts. Some years later a much larger deposit was found on the south bank of the Kuskokwim River, just north of Barometer Mountain.

Finally, in the early 1940's, a small deposit of cinnabar was found on one of the headwaters of the Holitna River, and a deposit of yet unknown size was discovered on Marsh Mountain at the east end of Lake Aleknagik. Mining and retorting continued intermittently at DeCourcy Mountain and on the Kuskokwim River from 1914 until the beginning of World War II when a great increase in the price of quicksilver caused renewed interest in the more promising deposits. A few flasks of quicksilver were produced from the small, high-grade deposit near the head of the Holitna River, and several thousand flasks were produced at the DeCourcy Mountain Mine and the Red Devil Mine near Barometer Mountain. Exploratory and development work at these two mines and at Marsh Mountain is still under way.

ROBERT M. CHAPMAN

Interior Highlands of Eastern Alaska

The interior highlands of eastern Alaska are rich in scenic beauty and historical interest, with fauna and flora to delight the sportsman, naturalist, and tourist. Here one interested in the development of Alaska can relive the incomparable days of the gold rush and have the thrill of panning gold. The miner or prospector can still go "out in the hills" in search of hidden lodes and placer deposits—and possibly be rewarded. The businessman and farmer can find new land in this fast-developing area. Many new roads and airfields are being built, and these, together with many navigable rivers and streams, give easy access to much of this "Golden Heart of Alaska" where the "cheechako" and "sourdough" meet.

The interior highlands of eastern Alaska are approximately bounded on the south by the meandering, braided courses of the Tanana and Yukon rivers, on the west by the extensive swampy lowlands adjacent to the lower Koyukuk River, on the north by the scenic south slope of the Brooks Range, and on the east by the Alaska-Canada boundary marked by a prominent man-cut swath through forest and brush that trends cross-country like an enormous ribbon. Within this vast area of approximately 68,000 square miles, great variation in scenery, geology, climate, and human endeavor is the rule.

The topography ranges from subdued rolling hills, covered with vegetation, to high rugged hills and mountains that reach far above the timber line where little or no vegetal cover masks the rocky crags and blocky talus slopes. The highest terrain generally lies in a west-trending belt that extends from the Canadian boundary between the Yukon and Tanana rivers to the Koyukuk River near the village of Hughes. This section is difficult to traverse. Many steep narrow valleys with small rushing creeks dissect the hills and mountains, and small patches of snow remain until midsummer in sheltered pockets on the highest peaks.

During the summer this high terrain is semiarid and quite barren, and many of the small creeks become dry. In late August and early September, it is frequently dusted with snow, foreboding the winter that does not invade the lower country until October. Early September is the ideal time to enjoy the area to the utmost. A riot of brilliant fall colors, rivaling those of New England, meets the eye. The summer green of the lowest hills and grassy tundra grades into the yellow of willows along the creeks and of birch and poplar trees on the lower slopes. Near the timber line the brilliant reds of the lower brush and small ground plants interrupt the leafy golden yellow, and the higher open slopes are a patchwork of red and maroon brush and light greenish-white moss and lichen, often grading into a snow-dusted background.

The lower rolling hills surrounding the rugged heart of this area are separated by innumerable small creeks, and by many large streams and navigable rivers some of which flow through sharp V-shaped valleys while others meander across wide, flat floors. The Yukon, Tanana, Koyukuk, and Porcupine rivers, as well as smaller rivers such as the Chena, Salcha, and Goodpaster, provide access to the hills.

Human activity is concentrated in the lower hilly country near the larger streams and rivers. The distribution of population in the early years of the century was influenced directly by the location of gold placers and by routes of travel between mining camps. Present settlements have grown around these early mining centers, but have been influenced greatly since 1942 by the wartime and postwar construction boom. Mining, which is chiefly geared to the fixed price of gold, declined to a secondary industry during World War II, and has failed to regain its former leading position. Many colorful mining communities and camps have, therefore, become ghost towns. Fur trapping, fishing, logging, and wood cutting, once the chief occupations for some white men and for most of the Indian natives, are other industries that have been left behind in the march of progress in interior Alaska.

The scenic, or more technically the geomorphic, features of the region have resulted from several geologic processes. Mountain-building movements that date far back into the geologic past, surficial weathering, and erosion, especially by processes peculiar to the subarctic, valley glaciation in restricted areas, changes in major river drainage patterns, and local deposition of wind-blown silt (loess)—all these processes acting on diverse kinds of rocks account for the variety of landscapes. There is much in common in the scenery of various parts, but for convenience in describing details it seems best to subdivide the region into five sections.

Section 1.—The western section, which lies roughly west of 153° West longitude and north of the Melozitna River, consists mostly of tree- and brush-covered, rounded hills between 1,000 and 3,000 feet in altitude. Because the relief is low to moderate and there are few rocky slopes or conspicuous hills, the landscape has a monotonous regularity. Most of the valleys are broad, and their gravel- and muck-covered floors are not sharply incised by streams. The rocks are conglomerates, sandstones and shales of Cretaceous age, intruded and locally altered by granites of Tertiary age. Unaltered sedimentary rocks, being relatively soft and therefore particularly likely to erode by frost action and water, produce subdued landforms, whereas granites and attendant metamorphosed rocks, being more resistant, form the highest hills in the western section, such as Indian Mountain near Hughes.

Section 2.—The west-central section, which lies south of the Melozitna and Koyukuk rivers, north of the Yukon River, and west of approximately 150° West longitude, is more rugged. The rocks have not yet been mapped in detail, partly because outcrops are scarce except on the highest hills, partly because the section is not easily accessible, and partly because only a few localities have shown promise of economic mineral deposits. It is known, however, that the chief rock types are schists of probable Precambrian age, granite and gneiss of probable early or middle Paleozoic age, and greenstones, which include altered lavas and tuffs, and locally some slate, chert, and impure limestone, probably of Devonian or Carboniferous age. Small patches of clay, shale, sandstone, conglomerate, and lignite beds of Tertiary age are present on the Yukon River near Rampart and Tanana, and one area of Tertiary or younger lavas is known near the Kanuti River.

The outstanding topographic features, such as the Ray Mountains and Kokrine Hills, consist of granitic rocks. The Ray Mountains rise conspicuously to altitudes of between 4,000 and 5,000 feet. Their bizarre rocky crags may be seen from the air or from high vantage points as much as 50 to 75 miles away, and in late August and early September their upper parts are often covered by a blanket of snow while the lower country is still bathed in the beauty of Indian summer.

Most of the hills do not rise above 2,000 to 3,000 feet and, to the dismay of the geologist, are almost uniformly covered by trees, brush, or tundra. The section is well dissected by several rivers and many smaller creeks. The river valleys are broad, swampy, and filled with silt, sand, gravel, and muck. A few of the small creek valleys near the Yukon River contain gold-bearing gravels, and the work of prospectors and miners is shown by pits, shafts, tailing piles, and log cabins, most of which are now being reclaimed by nature.

Local valley glaciers were present during the Pleistocene period in the Ray Mountains and Kokrine Hills; small cirques and some glacial debris can be seen in the higher parts of the latter, and cirques, hanging valleys, U-shaped glacial valleys, and morainal and outwash deposits lend a distinctive aspect to the former.

Section 3.—The southeastern section, called the Yukon-Tanana region by earlier writers, lies south of the Yukon River, almost entirely north of the Tanana River, and west of the Alaska-Canada boundary. The terrain here is made up largely of rounded hills of moderate altitude around a central area of high rugged hills and mountains. A small segment of low, flat, lake-dotted country adjacent to the upper Tanana River is included in the extreme southeastern corner of the area.

Much of the early gold prospecting and mining took place in this section. Such famous gold camps as Fairbanks, Rampart, Livengood, Tofty-Eureka, Circle, and Fortymile were well populated shortly after the turn of the century, and mining is still in progress at these and a few other places. The rivers, creeks, and hills are abundantly marked by the pits, portals, tailing piles, and dumps of the hardy pioneers.

Most parts of the section are easily accessible by automobile on the Alaska, Richardson, Steese, Elliott, and Taylor highways, and on numerous secondary roads and trails; by river boats on the Yukon and Tanana rivers;

by small shallow-draft boats on other rivers, such as the Chena, Salcha, and Goodpaster; and by bush airplanes that can land on small airfields. The high rugged country between the upper Charley River and the upper Chena River, between Eureka and Livengood, and between Livengood and Circle remains relatively inaccessible.

The arcuate group of hills that extends northeastward from Nenana and southeastward from the Steese Highway area to the border is underlain almost entirely by the Birch Creek schist of Precambrian age and by batholiths and smaller masses of granite, quartz diorite, and closely allied igneous rocks, mostly of Mesozoic age. Some of the rugged hilly and mountainous country in the drainage areas of the upper Chena and Salcha rivers, of the upper North Fork of Fortymile River, and of upper Beaver Creek is formed by slate, quartzite, chert, limestone, and phyllite showing various stages of metamorphism. This rather poorly known sequence of rocks is believed to be of pre-middle Ordovician age.

Smaller areas of greenstone and serpentine are found between the Chena and Salcha rivers; because they weather to yellowish-brown colors and form smooth rounded hilltops, they are readily distinguished from the schist, granite, and metamorphic rocks which form sharp rocky gray ridgetops. Volcanic rocks, mostly rhyolite and dacite, probably of Tertiary age, form prominent hills north of Tanacross and Tok Junction, and small areas of interlayered igneous and sedimentary rocks of Carboniferous and Devonian age form low hills just north of the Tanana River near Northway and Chicken.

The north-central and northwestern parts of the Yukon-Tanana region include a belt of high rugged hills and mountains difficult to traverse. The geology is complex, there being a great variety of sedimentary rocks and lava flows, some of which are slightly metamorphosed. These rocks are of Ordovician, Silurian, Devonian, and Carboniferous age. Accompanying them are a few small remnants of Tertiary sandstone, shale, and conglomerate, several small masses of granitic rocks of Mesozoic age, and isolated quartz monzonite intrusive bodies of Tertiary age.

The White Mountains, about 30 miles east of Livengood, are formed of Ordovician lavas, tuffs, and breccias, and of Silurian (Tolovana) limestone that weathers pale gray to white. No doubt, the mountains got their name because of their perpetually snowy appearance. The Crazy Mountains, 15 to 30 miles west of Circle, are an isolated group of prominent hills, between 3,000 and 3,700 feet high, that provide a scenic vista for the Circle Hot Springs area. They consist of greenstone, limestone, slate, tuff, and lava of

Devonian age, and limestone and interbedded sedimentary and volcanic rocks of Carboniferous age. Other prominent landmarks in the Rampart-Livengood area are Mount Schwatka (4,120 feet), formed of volcanic rocks and limestone of Devonian age, and the Sawtooth Mountains (4,800 feet), formed by an intrusion of quartz monzonite of Tertiary age.

The southwestern part of the Yukon-Tanana region differs geologically from the rest of the region. The general aspect is one of rounded, vegetated hills, and a few sharp, rocky peaks separated by broad valleys and wide swampy flats. A large part of the area is underlain by poorly exposed, quartz-rich sandstone, slate, and shale of Cretaceous age. Between Tolovana and Manley Hot Springs a group of hills, rising to approximately 2,000 feet, is formed by pre-middle Ordovician, Silurian, and Devonian rocks. The only prominent outcrops are those of the Tolovana limestone, which forms conspicuous light-gray, rubble-covered bands. The outstanding topographic features in this part of the Yukon-Tanana region are the high, talus-strewn Roughtop Mountain, Elephant Mountain, Wolverine Mountain, and Hot Springs Dome. These consist of Tertiary quartz-monzonite intrusions that are more resistant to erosion than the surrounding Cretaceous sedimentary rocks.

The Tofty-Eureka area has long been a gold and tin placer mining district, although the lode-source of the gold and cassiterite has never been found. A thick cover of vegetation and overburden greatly hampers exploration and low divides and the distribution of placer deposits indicate that major changes in the river drainage pattern occurred during Pleistocene time. The ancient drainage pattern of the Yukon-Tanana region is indeed one of the many challenging, unsolved geological problems of the interior highlands region.

Section 4.—The eastern section of the interior highlands of eastern Alaska lies between the Yukon and Porcupine rivers, and between the swampy Yukon Flats and the Canadian border. The general trend of the rock formations is east to northeast, as it is in the adjacent parts of Canada. Between the Yukon and Kandik rivers, especially near the border, the country is fairly rugged and quite rocky, and the hills, which range from 3,000 to 4,800 feet in altitude, make a formidable barrier to ground travel except along the major valleys.

Although the region is one of the more scenic parts of interior Alaska, it is seldom visited, and although it gives promise of being a possible petroleum province, it is poorly known geologically. Sedimentary and igneous rocks ranging in age from Cambrian to Tertiary are known to be present.

On and near the Tatonduk River, limestone, shale, argillite, and red beds of Cambrian age are exposed. In the rugged hills between the river and Eagle there are limestones and other sedimentary rocks of Paleozoic age, sandstone, shale, argillite, conglomerate, chert, and limestone of Devonian and Carboniferous age, as well as sandstone, shale, and conglomerate of Tertiary age. Between the Tatonduk and the Nation river drainages the formations are equally varied. Here are to be seen dolomite, quartzite, shale, laval flows, dikes, and sills, collectively assigned to the Tindir group, of Cambrian or Precambrian age. Here also are sedimentary rocks, including limestones, of Carboniferous and Permian age, and perhaps of older Paleozoic periods, and others of Triassic and Tertiary age. Throughout this section, light-colored, resistant limestones form conspicuous peaks and ridges.

Northwest of the Nation River drainage the hills are somewhat lower, few exceeding 4,000 feet in altitude. Most of them are rounded, and because they are nearly devoid of outcrops they are poorly known geologically. In contrast to the Tatonduk-Eagle area, the terrain here is monotonously uniform, because it is underlain by the Kandik formation, composed chiefly of sandstone and shale of Cretaceous age. Several large anticlinal structures, outlined by beds of limestone and traces of rubble, are conspicuous from the air. Still farther northwest the hills are 2,500 feet or less in altitude; these are underlain by the Kandik formation, and by early Carboniferous cherts, slates, shales, and volcanic rocks, including flows of basaltic lava and the fragmental products of explosive eruptions.

The area between the upper Kandik River and the Porcupine River is remote, seldom traveled, and little mapped. Most of the hills here range from 2,000 to 3,000 feet in altitude, only a few peaks near the boundary rising to greater heights. Between the Kandik River and Orange Creek, shale, sandstone, conglomerate, quartzite, slate, and limestone, probably of Cretaceous age, form low, barren hills with only a few outcrops of rock. To the east, in Canada, the country is much higher, and more rugged and scenic. To the north, in the upper Orange Creek and Black River area, there is an abrupt change into contorted metamorphic rocks, such as quartzite, slate, phyllite, and greenstone, belonging to the Tindir group of Cambrian or still greater age.

Between the Black and Porcupine rivers, and east of the mouth of the Coleen River, the geology is complex. Here are shales, sandstones, limestones, and their metamorphic equivalents, and basalt flows ranging in age from pre-Ordovician through Carboniferous, along with other basalt flows and shales, clays, marls, and lignites of Tertiary age. The rounded hills reveal few rock exposures, but the geology of the area can be partly interpreted from excellent outcrops along the sinuous, steep-walled canyon of the Porcupine River. These outcrops exhibit folds and faults of great complexity.

Section 5.—The northeastern section of the interior highlands of eastern Alaska lies east of approximately 150° West longitude, north of the Yukon Flats and Porcupine River, west of the Canadian boundary, and south of the higher foothills of the Brooks Range. Fur trappers, and miners and prospectors en route to the Chandalar and Wiseman placer gold mines, formerly traversed the area, but today there are probably fewer than fifty people in the entire section of about 15,000 square miles. It is accessible by small boat on the Coleen, Sheenjek, and Chandalar rivers, and although many old trails have been partly reclaimed by underbrush, ground travel is not difficult. Most of the hills are moderately rounded, and only the highest are devoid of small timber and underbrush. A few hills rise above 3,000 feet, but most range from 2,000 to 3,000 feet in altitude. Rock exposures are very scarce except in cut banks along rivers and creeks, and on the highest hills, where there are rocky knobs and slopes littered with frost-weathered talus.

Sedimentary rocks ranging in age from possible Precambrian through Carboniferous, and intrusive and volcanic rocks of Mesozoic and Tertiary age have been outlined on reconnaissance maps. Quartzite, schist, greenstone, and gneiss, perhaps equivalents of the Precambrian, Birch Creek schist of the Fairbanks area, form flat-topped hills just south of the Chandalar River, between the Middle Fork and the East Fork. They seem to dip northward beneath a northeast-trending belt of phyllite, schist, limestone, greenstone, and gneiss of early Paleozoic age that is exposed on the East Fork of the Chandalar River and near the Canadian border, north of the Porcupine River.

Just west of this belt, among the prominent hills along the East Fork, are outcrops of the conspicuous, light-gray, Skagit limestone of Silurian age. Between the East Fork and the Canadian border, a large area is underlain by sandstone, slate, and thin-bedded limestone of Devonian age that form low, almost featureless, rubble-laden hills. No doubt the structure here is complex, but the tundra cover conceals most of the evidence. Intrusions of diabase, perhaps of Devonian age, and quartzite, conglomerate, and slate of Mississippian age are also present in the area. The northern boundary is formed by foothills of light-gray Mississippian limestone and chert that resemble stepping stones leading to the majestic Brooks Range.

Strikingly rugged hills rise 4,000 to 5,000 feet on the south side of the Chandalar River near the abandoned village of Caro. These have been carved from the exposed part of a granite, or, more accurately, a granodiorite batholith intruded during the Mesozoic era. Several small patches of basaltic lava, erupted during the succeeding Tertiary era, form prominent red-weathering outcrops along the southern edge of this section.

Valley glaciers have played an important role in sculpturing the topography. Those that spread southward from the Brooks Range during the closing stages of the Pleistocene period left U-shaped valleys and moraines in their wake, and many lakes were formed in morainal depressions. Prominent terraces on the sides of many of the larger valleys testify to downcutting by streams as glacial conditions changed, and at Old John Lake, near the village of Arctic, three terraces mark higher levels of the shore.

Enough has been said to show that the interior highlands of eastern Alaska are geologically diverse and complex. They consist of igneous, sedimentary, and metamorphic rocks belonging to every geological age. Several famous placer gold mining districts lie within the region, and there are lode gold mines, a few stibnite and scheelite mines, as well as cassiterite, copper, lead, coal, and other prospects. In addition, the region is a potential source of petroleum. Technological developments and further exploration may well reveal new mineralized areas and extensions of previously known deposits.

Hardy miners and prospectors played a leading role in the original exploration and development of Alaska, as they did in the western United States and Canada. A second phase of development began during World War II and is now under way. Exploitation of mineral resources, though important, now plays a smaller part. As the construction boom begins to diminish, however, prospecting and mining will revive. Alaska will probably never again see an era to equal the gold rush of the early 1900's when remote valleys rang with the blows of prospectors' picks, but the advent of the Atomic Age will lead to search for minerals that formerly had little or no economic value. A new type of prospector, equipped with radiometric and airborne instruments, ultraviolet lights, chemical kits, and modern technical knowledge will replace the gold-hunter with his pick, shovel, and pan.

The eastern part of the interior highlands not only has mineral wealth but is endowed with hydroelectric power sites and has many hot springs that offer recreational possibilities. One of the great undeveloped hydroelectric dam sites of North America lies on the Yukon River, about 30 miles downstream from Rampart. A 290-foot dam at that point, where the Yukon River is confined in a relatively narrow, steep-walled valley, would impound a lake of about 7,000 square miles, extending upstream to the vicinity of Circle. Such a dam would generate annually more than eight billion kilowatt-hours of electricity. Other potential dam sites, as on Beaver Creek north of Fairbanks, and on the Tanana, Fortymile, Porcupine, Chandalar, Chena, Goodpaster, and Melozitna rivers, are available, though geological and surface-water studies must be made to evaluate the practicability of construction.

At least twelve hot springs have long been known in this region. Three of them, the Circle, Chena, and Manley hot springs, have been developed on a small scale for resort and bathing purposes, and further utilization is planned, but the potential of these and other hot springs has scarcely been realized either for local use or for attracting tourists. Copious supplies of water, ranging in temperature from 130° to 144° F. can be used for heating buildings and greenhouses and for warm baths and swimming pools. The warm water moreover flows throughout the winter, an important item in the subarctic, and it can be used in summer to irrigate gardens and stimulate plant growth, thus effectively lengthening the growing season. In addition, the ground temperature near the springs is appreciably higher than elsewhere, and most of the immediately adjacent areas are therefore devoid of permafrost. A few of the other undeveloped hot springs are favorably located for development, and the rest, though in remote areas, may someday be useful.

All of the springs issue from granitic intrusions or from closely adjacent rocks. Several iron, sulfur, and carbonate springs are known or reported, but they are not warm nor are they directly associated with granites.

Another geological factor that has an important bearing on economic development and land utilization in the interior highlands of eastern Alaska is permafrost, or perennially frozen ground. Most of the floodplains or valley floors and the low and intermediate hillslopes are perennially frozen below the limit of seasonal freezing and thawing. The lower limit of the frozen layer varies greatly, but perennial subfreezing temperatures generally extend to or into the underlying bedrock. Hilltops, high rocky ridges, and steep upper slopes may or may not be frozen. In the Fairbanks area most of the higher hilltops and south-facing slopes do not contain permafrost, but elsewhere permafrost has been found in underground mines and drill holes on the higher hills.

Frozen ground was both a hindrance and a help to the early placer miners. Prospect pits and underground drifts in muck and placer gravel had to be thawed foot by foot with steam or hot water. Once a hole or drift was opened, however, the surrounding ground remained frozen so that little if any support-timbering was necessary unless the opening was exposed to the summer heat for long periods. Much prospecting was done, therefore, during the winter with untimbered shafts.

Permafrost creates many difficulties for large-scale mining and for most construction. Nevertheless, only in recent years have geological and engineering studies been directed toward solving problems connected with construction of roads, railroads, airports, and buildings on unconsolidated or poorly consolidated material that includes permafrost. In placer mining there is but one solution—thaw the ground; however, to find the easiest and cheapest methods involves much work and experimentation. In many construction projects the permafrost problem is best handled by keeping the ground frozen, but few universal rules can be applied, and detailed studies are generally necessary to determine the best methods for handling particular conditions. Major problems affecting construction, farming, and water supply can often be surmounted with geological guidance by choosing alternate sites that present fewer difficulties.

Most tourists and cheechakos who see the interior highlands of eastern Alaska for the first time do so from the air or from an automobile. Air and car tours are provided commercially in Fairbanks, the hub of transportation and supply for the region, and a good generalized view of the country can be had on such trips. For those who wish more intimate knowledge or those who wish to hunt, fish, prospect, or explore more leisurely, private or chartered cars, boats, and bush planes are recommended.

One can view part of the region from modern airliners flying north from Seattle to Fairbanks. After crossing the Canada-Alaska boundary one sees to the north the rugged hills of the Fortymile district, which are largely composed of schist, and granitic and rhyolitic rocks. The usual flight path continues westward over the braided course of the silt-laden Tanana River, permitting views of the schist and granitic hills near the Goodpaster and Salcha rivers to the north. At the junction of the Alaska and Taylor highways and near Shaw Creek, old sand dunes, now largely covered by vegetation, are visible just north of the Tanana River.

From Fairbanks one can fly north to Fort Yukon, on the Yukon River just north of the Arctic Circle, in a swampy lowland known as the Yukon Flats. En route the plane passes over the placer mining area north of Fairbanks, and extensive dredge tailings may be seen in many valleys cut into the Birch Creek schist. The Steese Highway, which follows the general route of early-day foot, dog-team, and wagon travel between Circle and Fairbanks, winds through the placer mining area between the Chatanika River and Fairbanks.

Farther north the flight path crosses rugged hills between Beaver Creek and upper Preacher Creek, an area underlain by metamorphic rocks of pre-middle Ordovician age, granitic bodies, and sedimentary and volcanic rocks of Devonian and Carboniferous age.

On one leg of the trip to Fort Yukon, many tourists stop at Circle Hot Springs, a small settlement on the north slope of the schist and granite hills forming the backbone of the Yukon-Tanana region. The hot springs have been utilized for a long time, and considerable placer gold mining has centered thereabouts for many years.

Tourists who fly from Fairbanks to Nome and Kotzebue pass westward over hills of Birch Creek schist, then across the swampy Minto Lakes area and over rounded hills of sandstone and shale of Cretaceous age near Manley Hot Springs to the confluence of the Yukon and Tanana rivers where the town of Tanana is located. Between Tanana and Galena, en route to Nome, the plane usually flies along the Yukon River. Below one sees the route of the old telegraph line between Fairbanks and St. Michael, many old cabins that were "hotels" on the winter dog-team trail, a small placer gold mining area 30 to 40 miles west of Tanana, and the lonely settlements of Ruby and Kokrines.

The hills to the north, between Kokrines and the Tozitna River, consist of schist and greenstone cut by intrusions of granite, and the rugged peaks near Kokrines are largely composed of granitic rocks. Small cirques flanking the highest of these peaks indicate the presence of local glaciers during Pleistocene time. The Melozitna River, which enters the Yukon near Ruby, flows approximately along the contact between the schist and granite of the Kokrine Hills and the sandstone, shale, and conglomerate of Cretaceous age which form the lower rounded hills between the Melozitna and Koyukuk rivers.

A recently established tourist trip between Fairbanks and Barrow provides an excellent opportunity to see much of the geology and scenery of the interior highlands of eastern Alaska as well as the interior lowlands, the Brooks Range, and the Arctic Slope. The flight path north from Fairbanks crosses belts of Birch Creek schist, metamorphic rocks of pre-middle Ordovician age, and Siluro-Devonian sedimentary rocks, including prominent beds of limestone, before reaching the placer gold mining area at Livengood. Between this point and the Yukon River the scenic hills are made up of chert, limestone, other sedimentary rocks, and basaltic tuffs, breccias, and lava flows of Mississippian age.

At the Yukon River one can look upstream and see braided channels wandering through the swampy Yukon Flats, and then look downstream and see a single broad ribbon of water winding through the hills. This contrast is an inheritance from the meandering course originally established by the river on an old Tertiary land surface since destroyed by erosion. In geological terms, the Yukon is here a superimposed river.

Between the Yukon River and Bettles, an early trading center in the upper Koyukuk mining region, the hills are moderately high and monotonously similar. They are composed chiefly of schist, limestone, quartzite, and greenstone of early Paleozoic or Precambrian age, granite of possible Mesozoic age, and basaltic lavas of probable Tertiary age. Near the Yukon River the high, rough peaks of the Ray Mountains can be seen in the western distance. These are composed largely of granitic rocks. Just north of Bettles, before entering the Brooks Range province, one sees rounded hills formed of sandstone, shale, and conglomerate of Cretaceous age.

For those who travel by car from Fairbanks, many miles of good road are available during the summer months. Between Fairbanks and Livengood, the road passes the Engineer Creek area where a large dredge may be seen digging gold-bearing gravels that were only partly mined out by hand methods in the early days. The gold placer gravels are here overlain by 30 to 40 feet of muck, a mixture of silt and vegetal material. This cover, which is barren of gold and perennially frozen, is removed by hydraulic nozzling, by stripping the surface vegetation and by solar thawing. Banks of the muck are visible at the sides of the valley.

Between Fox and the Chatanika River bridge small and large mining operations can be seen on both sides of the road, many of them now abandoned. At Olnes, near the bridge, only a few cabins remain of a once large and thriving town that was a center of activity in the Dome Creek mining area. Between Fox and Washington Creek, the Birch Creek schist is exposed in several road cuts, and on the north side of Globe Creek, the Tolovana limestone, of Silurian age, is prominent in many exposures. Between the Tatalina River and Livengood very little rock is exposed, but the hills are part of a belt of slate, chert, and quartzite of probable Devonian age.

Livengood, now almost a ghost town, lies in the valley of Livengood Creek. Chert and limestone of Mississippian age form ridges on the north side and upper part of the creek. The placer gravels of the valley and tributaries yielded rich deposits of gold between 1914 and 1941, but dredging operations on Livengood Creek since 1946 have proved disappointing, and there is now very little activity in the area.

The trip from Fairbanks to Circle on the Steese Highway follows the historic route of the gold stampeders. Today, gold mining is restricted to the areas around Fairbanks, Faith Creek, Miller House, and Circle Hot Springs, where granitic-type rocks and associated mineralized quartz veins cut the Birch Creek schist. Between Fox and Chatanika evidence of past and present lode and placer mining is widespread. In addition to gold, small deposits of antimony, tungsten, and lead have been mined with limited success around Pedro Dome, about 23 miles from Fairbanks. Along the highway between Pedro Dome and the head of the Chatanika River one can see the Davidson Ditch, which carries water about 74 miles to the United States Smelting, Refining, and Mining Company's operations in the Fairbanks area.

With the exception of the granitic rocks mentioned above, all exposures of bedrock on the Steese Highway are of the Birch Creek schist of Precambrian age. Between Miller House and Circle, the Crazy Mountains loom prominently to the north. They are made up of sedimentary and volcanic rocks of Devonian and Mississippian age. The broad swampy alluvial flats between Central and Circle were formed as flood plain and channel deposits of the Yukon River in post-Tertiary time.

A trip from Fairbanks to the Canadian border via the Richardson and Alaska highways offers much of scenic and historic interest. The road generally follows the braided course of the silt-laden Tanana River, so that most of the bedrocks can be seen only on distant hills. Between Fairbanks and Big Delta, the Birch Creek schist is exposed, except near Harding Lake and Birch Lake where granitic rock can be seen in man-made cuts near the highway. The Tenderfoot and Banner creeks placer gold mining area is located near Richardson Roadhouse, about 64 miles from Fairbanks.

From Robertson River to Midway Lake the hills north of the road are composed of intrusive granitic and extrusive rhyolitic rocks. Granitic rocks also form the Tanana River bluffs. Between Midway Lake and the Canadian border outcrops are rare, but some greenstone, slate, schist, and granitic rocks can be noted in roadcuts. A prominent, thin, grayish-white layer of volcanic ash, laid down about fourteen hundred years ago, lies immediately beneath the turf and is revealed in many roadcuts. Apparently it was laid down during explosions of a volcano, now inactive, in the St. Elias Mountains about 150 miles to the south.

At Fortymile Roadhouse, about 80 miles from the Canadian boundary, the Taylor Highway, which links Eagle and Dawson in the Yukon Territory with the Tanana Valley, winds northward from the Alaska Highway through the beautiful Fortymile area and mining district. For the first 5 miles, the highway passes through sand dunes deposited in Pleistocene time by winds that carried material northward from the extensive glacial outwash in the Tanana Valley. Granitic and rhyolitic rocks form the hills between the Tanana River and the West Fork of the Dennison Fork. Granitic rocks also make up the 5,400-foot peak of Mount Fairplay, the most conspicuous topographic feature in the Dennison Fork area. Near the West Fork of the Dennison Fork, the road traverses Birch Creek schist and then crosses granitic rocks north of the river.

Many rock types are to be seen near Chicken, among them metamorphic rocks of Devonian age, and rhyolite, sandstone, shale, and conglomerate of Tertiary age. This is one of the oldest centers of placer mining in Alaska, gold having been discovered on Franklin Creek, 6 miles north of Chicken, in 1886. Between Chicken and the Canadian border there are several almost deserted towns and numerous mines, many of which have been exhausted or abandoned. From the South Fork of Fortymile River to the border, the bedrock is the familiar Birch Creek schist, intruded by many small granitic masses.

The road to Eagle runs northward through high, picturesque country that has long been traveled by prospectors. In addition to crossing Birch Creek schist, it traverses a belt of metamorphic rocks of Devonian age and a narrow strip of sandstone, shale, and conglomerate of Tertiary age on American Creek.

The visitor is likely to marvel at the names of many of the rivers, creeks, towns, and other features he encounters in his travels. Some of the names are common and unimaginative. For instance, the names Slate, Quartz, Granite, Gold, Discovery, Nugget, Coal, Moose, Caribou, Bear, Grouse, Ptarmigan, Mosquito, Alder, Spruce, and Birch are repeated many times within the interior highlands of eastern Alaska and many more times throughout the Territory. Some original Indian names, such as Tanana,

Chena, Tatalina, Hutlinana, Melozitna, and Sheenjek have been preserved, but more often they have been replaced by English translations or by simpler names. Early prospectors, thinking nostalgically of home, coined such creek names as California, Idaho, Montana, Buckeye, Homestake, and Eureka, and the patriotism and political consciousness of old timers are recalled by names like Uncle Sam, Liberty, Independence, Yankee, Confederate, and Democrat. One creek in the Fortymile district bears the optimistic name of Wall Street! The inner feelings of lonely prospectors are reflected in many women's names applied to creeks.

Other names, such as Hard Luck, Last Chance, Troublesome, Starvation, Frozen-foot, and Helpmejack, speak of the difficulties and despair of some of the pioneers, whereas happier times are suggested by festive names such as Fourth of July, Thanksgiving, Merry Christmas, and Happy Near Year creeks. Tongue-in-cheek humor appears as Big Sitdown Creek, and Bottom Dollar Creek that has tributaries called Half Dollar and Two-Bit creeks. And, who knows?—perhaps such creek names as King Solomon, Queen of Sheba, Omega, Faith, Hope, and Charity were conjured up by bearded prospectors around a flickering campfire.

J. P. HOPKINS AND D. M. HOPKINS

Seward Peninsula

Seward Peninsula is a remote westward projection of the Alaskan mainland. No roads link it to the rest of Alaska; indeed until about 1940, Nome could be reached only by boat or by dog team. Today, most of the peninsula's food and manufactured goods arrive by ship during the short, ice-free summer, and most visitors arrive by airplane.

The peninsula has been an important center of Eskimo population throughout recorded history. The first permanent European settlement was established in 1881, when a trading post was opened at Cheenik on Golovnin Bay. During the next two decades only a small number of Europeans lived on the peninsula, but the discovery of large and rich gold placers in 1898 assured the peninsula a relatively large Caucasian population ever since.

Geologists, paleontologists, zoölogists, plant geographers, and anthropologists find special interest in the Seward Peninsula because of all parts of North America it lies closest to Asia. Shallow seas that now surround it and extend to the Siberian coast were probably dry land during glacial periods when sea level was lower than at present. The peninsula then formed the backbone of a land bridge across which plants and animals were exchanged between the two continents (see map 5 and fig. 3). Man himself probably first entered North America across this bridge shortly before it was drowned by rising seas, as glaciers began to melt about 10,000 years ago. We may therefore expect some day to find North America's oldest human remains on or near Seward Peninsula.

The peninsula is roughly rectangular, measuring about 200 miles long from east to west and 120 miles wide from north to south, and its northernmost point, Cape Espenberg, lies on the Arctic Circle. To the south, the peninsula is bounded by Bering Sea and to the north by the Chukchi Sea. When the weather permits, one can stand on Cape Prince of Wales at the western tip of the peninsula and look across the gray waters of Bering Strait to the subdued mountains of East Cape in Siberia, only 50 miles away.

Most of Seward Peninsula consists of extensive uplands surmounted by groups of rugged mountains. Lowland basins occupy the interior, low plains fringe much of the coast, and a wide lava plateau surrounds Imuruk Lake in the north-central part.

Much of the upland area is made up of broad, convex hills and ridges separated by sharply V-shaped valleys. South of Port Clarence and west of Cape Darby, however, the uplands are more rugged, convex hills and ridges being separated by steep-walled, but wider floored, valleys. Mount Osborn (4,720 feet) in the Kigluaik Mountains is the peninsula's highest point; few other peaks rise above 3,000 feet, and the general relief is less than 2,000 feet.

The prominent highland groups are the York, the Kigluaik (or Sawtooth), the Bendeleben, and the Darby Mountains. The York Mountains are an oval range near Cape York. The Kigluaik Mountains form an east-west range roughly parallel to and 20 to 30 miles north of the coast of Norton Sound. They are separated from the Bendeleben Mountains, farther northeast, by a lowland less than 400 feet above sea level at its highest point. The Darby Mountains, still farther east, trend north-south and together with the Bendeleben Mountains form a crescentic chain open to the southwest and extending to the coast of Norton Sound. Before the Pleistocene period, these four mountain ranges were probably rolling highlands that owed their relief to the resistant nature of the rocks of which they are composed. Much of their present height results, however, from Pleistocene uplift ranging from several hundred to a thousand feet.

In contrast with the mountainous highlands are several broad basins dotted with lakes and floored with alluvium and glacial sediments. A chain of lowlands extends southeast from the drowned valley occupied by Grantley Harbor and Salt Lake (or Imuruk Basin) to Golovnin Bay, fresh fault scarps bounding the south margins near Salt Lake and Council. Another series of isolated lowland basins completely surrounded by highlands comprises the upper Fish River lowland, the Kuzitrin flats, and the Agiapuk River lowland. Other interior lowlands are scattered throughout the peninsula.

The north coast of Seward Peninsula west of Cape Espenberg is a low-lying plain as much as 30 miles wide, fringed along much of its extent by barrier bars enclosing a series of lagoons. Smaller coastal plains fringe the south coast near Cape Wooley, Nome, Solomon, Moses Point, and Koyuk. Elsewhere the coast is rugged, and valley mouths are either deeply indented or floored by broad expanses of alluvium. From Cape Prince of Wales to Teller, an extensive deformed marine terrace carved in bedrock, the York terrace, lines the coast.

The bedrocks of Seward Peninsula are much more like those of the Chukotski Peninsula in Siberia than those of adjoining parts of the Alaskan mainland. Most of the peninsula is underlain by schist or slate. Limestone underlies the York Mountains and several other large upland areas. Granite is common in the Kigluaik, the Bendeleben, and the Darby Mountains, and small bodies are present elsewhere. Sandstone, shale, and conglomerate of Cretaceous age extend from Norton Bay to the southeast corner of Kotzebue Sound. Basalt lavas of Pleistocene age cover about 1,000 square miles near Imuruk Lake and a smaller area along the Koyuk River near Haycock, and volcanic ash covers several hundred square miles near Devil Mountain. Most of the lowlands and coastal plains in the southern part of the peninsula are underlain by coarse gravel, whereas most of those in the northern part are underlain by thick deposits of silt.

Many of the communities on the Seward Peninsula own their existence to rich strikes of gold. The metal was deposited originally in quartz veins cutting the schist bedrocks. During many thousands of years both the veins and enclosing schists were fragmented by frost action on hillsides, and the resultant debris was moved by creep and soil flowage into the valley bottoms to be washed and sorted by streams. Although the quartz grains and other light-weight rock fragments were quickly transported seaward, much of the gold remained behind as alluvial placers in the gravels on the stream beds or collected along ancient coasts as beach placers, along with magnetite, garnet, and other heavy minerals.

Except for the Big Hurrah Mine near Solomon, the bedrock gold veins have proved too small, too widely scattered, and too low in grade for profitable mining; almost all the rich gold strikes have been of placer type.

Gold was probably discovered on Seward Peninsula in 1865 or 1866 by a survey party led by Baron von Bendeleben, who was seeking a route for the proposed intercontinental line of the Russian-American Telegraph Company. This early discovery aroused no public attention, and no attempt at exploitation or further exploration was made until about 1892. A little prospecting and probably a little mining were done during the early 1890's by persons engaged chiefly in other activities, but the gold rush did not start in earnest until the discovery in 1898 of rich placers near Council and Nome, the setting of Rex Beach's book *The Spoilers*. By 1900, gold had been found in many other parts of the peninsula. The summer population of Nome then reached a probable peak of 20,000, and annual gold production climbed to nearly $5,000,000.

In subsequent years, as better mining methods and mechanical equipment came into use, more gold was mined by fewer people, and during the height of the gold-mining era, from 1905 to 1930, dredges were installed on nearly all of the significant gold-producing streams. Among the most characteristic cultural features of the Seward Peninsula are dredges working on the few streams where large-scale mining is still in progress, and rotting hulks of idle dredges on streams that can no longer be mined with profit.

The western tip of the peninsula contains the principal tin-mining district in the United States. Placer tin was observed in the York Mountains in 1900 by Dr. A. H. Brooks of the U.S. Geological Survey, and lode tin was reported three years later by other Survey geologists. The placer deposits have been mined profitably during several periods of high prices in the present century, and lode tin has been produced at Lost River since World War II.

High mining costs resulting from remoteness of the region, poor inland transportation, and unfavorable climate have prevented extensive exploitation of other mineral resources. A lead-zinc deposit at Omilak in the Darby Mountains was among the earliest mineral discoveries in Alaska, and although attempts at mining were undertaken as early as 1881, they never progressed beyond the development stage. Small quantities of lode antimony and placer tungsten have been mined during periods of high prices in the Snake River and the Nome River valleys, and platinum has been recovered as a by-product of placer gold operations in the Haycock-Peace River area in the southeastern part of the peninsula. Coal has been mined in the valley of the Kugruk River on a small scale for local consumption during most of the period since 1903.

The visitor to Seward Peninsula is likely to be impressed by abundant landscape features resulting from intense frost action and the presence of perennially frozen ground. In most places the ground remains frozen to depths of 100 feet or more, only the upper few feet of the soil thawing each summer.

Large and small masses of ice are present in the perennially frozen ground, or permafrost, commonly comprising as much as a third of the total volume of the soil. When such ice-laden ground thaws, the surface subsides and small lakes are likely to be formed. These "thaw lakes" then grow by caving of their banks until they are drained and their bottoms refreeze. Many lowland areas consist almost entirely of thaw lakes, and the basins of drained thaw lakes formed in this way.

Shallow permafrost poses serious problems to most communities on Seward Peninsula as well as in other parts of central and northern Alaska. Because the ground is frozen, domestic water wells cannot be developed, and few communities have public water distribution or sewage-disposal systems owing to the prohibitive cost of construction and winter operation. Heated buildings thaw the frozen ground beneath them and settle as the ice melts. Several large public buildings, including the Federal Building in Nome, have sagged differentially as much as several feet and now have sharply tilted floors and badly fractured foundations and walls. Many small frame houses in Nome rest on mechanical jacks; taking a few turns on the jack to level up the kitchen is as familiar a summer activity to the Nome householder as is mowing the lawn to the average suburbanite in the States.

Ice-wedge polygons are a striking and ubiquitous feature of many Seward Peninsula landscapes. They cover most lowlands and gentle slopes in the northern part and are common in marshes in the southern part. Winters are cold enough in these places to cause the ground to contract and crack. Snow then blows into the cracks and hoarfrost condenses on their walls to form thin vertical veins of ice. During the summer, the upper parts of the ice veins thaw, while the lower parts remain intact within the permafrost. Repetition of this process produces wedges of ice 5 to 10 feet wide and 10 to 15 feet deep, arranged in honeycomblike polygons. At the surface, the position of the wedges is marked by shallow, damp trenches where the vegetation is a little greener or a little darker than it is on the adjoining higher ground. This makes the polygons strikingly obvious when viewed from the air.

One is generally impressed, while flying over the peninsula, by the widespread signs of rapid movement of soil off hilltops, down slopes, and into valley bottoms. On hilltops, the rocky soils are arranged in frost-heaved stone polygons, much smaller and more irregular than ice-wedge polygons. On slopes, the stone polygons are drawn out into rectangles and then into stripes extending directly downslope. Finer-grained soils show frost-heaved vegetation polygons on summits, drawn-out ones on gentle slopes, and closely spaced stripes of contrasting vegetation on steeper slopes. On other hills and ridges, clusters of bushes are arranged in garlands and festoons along the edges of stepped or tonguelike masses of soil that appear to have wrinkled and buckled as they moved irregularly downslope as slow mud-flows.

All these features reflect the profound disturbance caused in the upper few feet of the soil by annual cycles of freezing and thawing. To the casual observer, they give a somewhat exaggerated impression of the rate of movement, for in most places individual soil particles actually move less than an inch a year. Nevertheless, this downslope migration of the soil mantle is rapid compared to the almost infinitesimally slow soil movements on comparable slopes in more temperate regions. It results in part from creep brought about by frost-heaving in the fall and subsidence during spring, and in part from actual flowage of thoroughly saturated soil when snow melts and ice masses thaw in the near-surface layers.

Most of Seward Peninsula has a more or less complete cover of tundra vegetation, and sparse forests are found in the southeastern part. A few areas, however, are nearly devoid of vegetation. The youngest lava flows in the Imuruk Lake area remain almost as they were when they solidified a thousand years ago. Slightly older lava flows have been reduced by frost action to vast expanses of loose, open rubble, but these also have no soil and bear no vegetation except lichens. Several large upland tracts under-lain by limestone are desertlike expanses with rugged, barren ridges of white rock and gravelly alluvial fans supporting only a few isolated shrubs and scattered patches of dwarf, tufted plants.

Several mineralized hot springs have been popular resorts for prospectors, miners, and other residents of Seward Peninsula. Some miners in the Kougarok placer district still make an annual fall pilgrimage to Serpentine Hot Springs after cold weather has stopped their mining operations. They bask in the baths until the warm waters loosen their kinked and tired muscles, which have become tightened by a summer of unremitting labor moving dirt and washing gold. Pilgrim Hot Springs near Salt Lake was an even more popular sourdough resort in past decades. The warm springs there seep diffusely through thick layers of gravel, warming the soil suf-ficiently to bring summer to an area about a mile square several weeks before it arrives in nearby areas. Indeed, a large grove of poplars and aspens growing in the hottest area gives Pilgrim Hot Springs an atmosphere of tropical luxuriance compared to the treeless tundra of the surrounding region.

Much of Seward Peninsula is accessible only by air to the tourist and casual traveler, but several interesting areas can be reached by automobile over gravel roads radiating from Nome. The large dredges of the United States Smelting, Refining, and Mining Company operate within 3 miles of the city; smaller dredges and hydraulic mining operations can be seen on Anvil and Glacier creeks and in the Nome River Valley north of Nome, and in the valley of the Solomon River, a few hours drive to the east. The rugged and beautiful Kigluaik Mountains are crossed by a highway following the grade of the now-abandoned Seward Peninsula Railroad. The effects of frost action and rapid soil movement may be seen on hillsides along the highway south of the mountains, and ice-wedge polygons and thaw lakes are abundant near the road in the Pilgrim River lowland north of the mountains. Travel on Seward Peninsula is not easy, but anyone who explores the country around Nome with initiative and imagination will be rewarded by views of varied and colorful tundra landscape and a picturesque mining industry not duplicated close to any other Alaskan city.

GEORGE GRYC

Brooks Range

The Brooks Range, a rugged glaciated mountain barrier, extends west from the Canadian border almost completely across northern Alaska to the Arctic Ocean, separating the virtually uninhabited arctic tundra lands from the more populated parts of interior Alaska. By denying easy access, it helps to preserve one of the last large wilderness areas of the Territory. Although not as high as other mountain ranges in Alaska, it is the highest within the Arctic Circle, and for this reason is unique in many respects.

Because the Brooks Range is largely devoid of trees, it presents a naked view of the stuff of which it is made. And although it is largely underlain by permanently frozen ground and blanketed by snow, ice, and almost total darkness during much of the year, the remaining months are marked by almost continuous sunlight and sufficient rain to change the bleak tundra into a carpet of miniature flowering plants. Birds of many kinds nest here, and herds of statuesque caribou pass by on their annual migrations. In its unique arctic environment of extreme contrasts, the Brooks Range thus offers unusual recreational possibilities.

The range was named for Alfred H. Brooks, former chief of the Alaskan Branch of the U.S. Geological Survey. It consists of many individual mountain groups. The Romanzof and the Davidson Mountains rise at the east

111

end of the range; the Franklin, the Shublik, and the Sadlerochit Mountains lie in the Canning River drainage system; the newly named Philip Smith Mountains (named for Philip S. Smith, successor to Brooks as chief of the Alaskan Branch of the U.S. Geological Survey) are at the head of the Canning and Sagavanirktok rivers; the Endicott Mountains are in the central part of the range, and the DeLong, Baird, and Schwatka Mountains form the west end. Together these mountain groups comprise the Alaskan counterpart of the Rocky Mountains of the western United States and Canada.

The Brooks Range, like all other Alaskan ranges, describes a huge arc. The DeLong Mountains, at the west end, swing southwest, and the Romanzof and the Davidson Mountains, at the opposite end, merge with the British and the Richardson Mountains which swing sharply south into the Rocky Mountains of Canada. The relatively smooth arc of the range is broken by a pronounced northward bulge in the Canning River region. East of the 149th meridian, the north front of the range swings sharply north around the bulge; the south front continues in a general easterly direction. The west end is bisected by the Noatak River, the only major river that lies entirely in the Brooks Range.

The highest peaks in the range are to be found in the Canning River region. These are Mount Chamberlin in the Franklin Mountains and Mount Michelson in the adjoining Romanzof Mountains, both of which rise a little more than 9,000 feet high. The peaks generally become lower westward to 6,000 and 7,000 feet in the Endicott Mountains, although Mount Doonerak is about 8,800 feet high. Still farther west, in the DeLong Mountains, the summits are more subdued, ranging in height between 3,000 and 4,000 feet.

Many small cliff and valley glaciers set in oversized cirques and troughs in the eastern half of the range testify to previous widespread glaciation. West of the Killik River, glaciers are almost entirely absent, partly because the altitude diminishes in that direction. This explains the smoother sculpturing of the DeLong Mountains as compared with the saw-toothed appearance of the Endicott and the Romanzof Mountains.

Much has still to be learned concerning the geology of the Brooks Range, but the major rock formations have already been mapped and described. The backbone of the range is composed of limestone, quartzite, and metamorphic rocks dating back to the Silurian, Devonian, and Mississippian periods, about 240 to 360 million years ago. The younger rocks that flank the range include sandstone, conglomerate, and shale, as well as unusual sediments such as oil shale and phosphatic limestone; these date back to the Permian, Triassic, Jurassic, and early Cretaceous periods, 70 to 210 million years ago.

The oldest rocks show that about 360 million years ago the region was occupied by a vast seaway in which were deposited sediments derived from lands to the north and west. Marine deposition continued with only minor interruptions until the Jurassic period, approximately 130 to 155 million years ago, when the region was uplifted to form the ancestral Brooks Range. These mountain-building movements were gentle at first but increased in intensity until mid-Cretaceous time, about 80 to 100 million years ago, when the ancestral range was strongly folded and faulted, and its marine sediments were metamorphosed and intruded by molten masses.

As these disturbances continued, the rising range was eroded, and sediments were transported northward from its flanks into a shallow seaway, which covered areas that formerly had been land. Periodic uplift persisted throughout Cretaceous time, and during the early part of the succeeding Tertiary era, some 60 million years ago, the range was once more strongly deformed and elevated, only to be eroded again to an area of low relief.

Not until late Tertiary time, between 10 and 20 million years ago, did the Brooks Range acquire its present form as a high, mountainous region. Renewed uplift, erosion, and glaciation since that time account for the rugged profiles one sees today.

From a structural viewpoint, the range is an elevated geanticline squeezed into tight folds and sliced by faults into sheets that have been shuffled together like a deck of cards.

The foregoing summary is based on the work of many geologists and explorers over a period of more than fifty years. Until recently the range was accessible only by long and arduous travel; today, however, it can be seen in a few hours' trip by air in relative ease. Much of it can be reached by use of bush planes, and boat traverses are possible over several routes. As a result, part of the complex geological history of the range can now be quickly discerned.

Glacial lakes provide the easiest access. These bodies of water, sometimes a clear blue-green, and at other times milky, lie in mountain valleys gouged by ancient glaciers, where melting ice dumped its morainic debris in the path of former streams. Several such lakes in the eastern half of the range are suitable for large float-plane landings in the summer, and for ski- and possibly wheel-plane landings in the winter. They include the following:

Chandler Lake, at the head of the Chandler River; Wild Lake in the John River drainage system; Shainin Lake near Anaktuvuk Pass; Chandalar Lake and Old John Lake in the Chandalar River drainage system; and Lake Peter and Lake Schrader at the foot of Mount Chamberlin. Several smaller lakes are suitable for small float planes.

In the western half of the range, lakes are less common, but the few are especially worth noting. They include Kurupa Lake, at the head of the Kurupa River; Nigu Lake, at the head of the Nigu River in the western part of the Endicott Mountains; Howard Lake, in Howard Pass in the eastern part of the DeLong Mountains; several lakes in the upper Noatak River system, including Feniak Lake; and Lake Walker, Lake Selby, Lake Nutuvukti, and Lake Norutak, on the south side of the Schwatka Mountains.

Although the high peaks and deeply trenched valleys of the Brooks Range make formidable barriers to easy ground traverse, there are many passes formed by a combination of glacial and stream erosion which can be traversed with reasonable facility. Perhaps the best and most widely known of these is Anaktuvuk Pass, at an altitude of only 2,200 feet, between the north-flowing Anaktuvuk River and the south-flowing John River. It is commonly used by small bush planes and is also on the main route of large aircraft bound for Barrow and other points on the arctic coast. The only inland group of Eskimos in Alaska live in the pass and in the valley of the Anaktuvuk River just to the north. Weasels (fully tracked military vehicles) can be driven through the pass, and portage from the John River to the Anaktuvuk River can be made with relative ease.

Other feasible portage routes through the mountains west of Anaktuvuk Pass are as follows: by way of the Alatna River and its tributary, the Anakserak River, to the Killik River over a pass at 3,800 feet; by way of a small tributary of the Alatna to the Noatak River over a pass at about 3,400 feet; and by way of tributaries of the Noatak River, the Aniuk, Nimiuktuk, and Kugurorok rivers through low passes at 2,200, 3,800, and 2,600 feet, respectively, to tributaries of the Colville and Utukok rivers. From Anaktuvuk Pass eastward to the Kongakut River there appear to be no gaps suitable for easy ground traverse. There is a low pass at approximately 2,500 feet between the Firth and Kongakut rivers and another from the Firth into the Coleen River. Except for this area of low passes, the eastern Brooks Range is not readily traversable either on the ground or by small bush plane and consequently is relatively unknown.

The Brooks Range is the backbone that separates waters flowing southward into the Yukon and its tributaries and westward into Kotzebue Sound from those flowing northward into the Arctic Ocean. Many large and readily navigable rivers begin in the range. The Noatak River flows west through the range for almost its entire course, and is traversable by boat or canoe as far up as Portage Creek. Its major tributaries, the Aniuk, Nimiuktuk, and Kugururok, are traversable with reasonable ease for about half their lengths; the rest can be traversed with considerable difficulty at high water. The major south-flowing tributaries of the Koyukuk and Yukon rivers—the Alatna, John, Wild, Chandalar, Sheenjek, and Coleen—some of which are swift and turbulent near the crest of the range, are traversable by boat or canoe.

The north slope of the Brooks Range is drained primarily by the Colville River and its major tributaries, the Nuka, Kiligwa, Ipnavik, Etivluk, Killik, Chandler, Anaktuvuk, and Itkillik rivers. The Colville River and all of its major, and most of its minor, tributaries have been traversed by Geological Survey parties. Other major north-flowing rivers, such as the Sagavanirktok, Canning, Sadlerochit, Hulahula, Okpilak, Jago, and Kongakut, are traversable north of the range with reasonable facility but are swift and turbulent where they flow through glacial debris at the mountain front. Within the range the rivers are generally braided, and except during high water are frequently too shallow for watercraft, apart from light boats or canoes. Near the drainage divide the stream gradients steepen, sometimes rather rapidly, resulting in canyons with swift, turbulent water.

Several Alaskan bush-plane airlines have pilots who are experienced and familiar with at least part of the range, and regularly scheduled tours are now available from Fairbanks to Fort Yukon on the Yukon River, to Kotzebue at the western end of the Brooks Range, and to Point Barrow, the northernmost tip of Alaska.

The flight to Barrow affords a particularly good opportunity to study the contrast of the wooded interior highlands of Alaska with the barren mountain and tundra regions of the arctic. A direct flight from Fairbanks to Barrow passes over the Livengood gold placer district, across the Yukon River near Stevens Village, and then on to Bettles, the last check point before entering the range. On a clear day the plane will probably fly a short distance above the peaks, or on an exceptional day, possibly through Anaktuvuk Pass, below the peaks. If visibility is good, light-colored limestones can easily be distinguished from dark quartzites and slates that form prominent hogback ridges. South of the crest, along the John River, one sees the oldest rocks in the range; near the crest the rocks become progressively younger, and as the plane emerges on the north side darker outcrops of the youngest rocks come into view.

Some impression of the complex structure of the range can be gained by observing the steep angles at which the beds are tilted and the many abrupt changes from limestone to slate and quartzite. High-level cirques, huge bowllike depressions, isolated peaks, and broad U-shaped valleys, such as that of the Anaktuvuk River, bear witness to erosion by powerful glaciers. The John River, on the south side of the range, has a characteristic U-shaped profile as far south as the Hunt Fork, but beyond, owing to recent uplift and consequent rapid erosion, it flows through a steep-walled canyon cut in glacial debris.

A trip through Anaktuvuk Pass by small bush plane permits closer inspection of the geologic features. Small float planes can be landed on Summit Lake within the pass or on Tulugak Lake near the front of the range, and small encampments of inland Eskimos lie within easy walking distance, though their presence tends to keep away game animals. One of the most striking features both from the air and on the ground is the amazingly abrupt northern limit of the spruce trees, coinciding almost exactly with the drainage divide. No spruce or other evergreens than scrub juniper have been recorded north of the divide, except on Joe and Mancha creeks near the Canadian border. Willows up to 20 feet high and poplars up to 35 feet high have been seen in small local areas.

Trips by boat or canoe may be made on the John and Anaktuvuk rivers, but they should be undertaken only by those experienced in camping and used to rough water. A boat may be taken up the John River for some distance with relative ease, although a trip all the way to the pass requires some portaging and "lining." It is quicker and more pleasant to start by boat at one of the lakes and go downstream to where a bush plane pick-up can be arranged, but such a trip should be planned with an experienced pilot.

Float planes of considerable size can land on Shainin Lake, only 15 airline miles east of the Anaktuvuk River. This lake lies in a smaller and narrower valley than that of the Anaktuvuk River; consequently the surrounding peaks and ridges lie closer to the water. Here, within easy walking distance, one may study a well-exposed section of Mississippian rocks, including fossiliferous limestones laid down in an ancient, pre-Brooks Range seaway. Many glacial features, such as cirques, arêtes, hanging valleys, and morainal deposits, can also be reached in a few hours' walk, and small remnant glaciers can be seen among the high peaks 15 to 20 miles south of the lake.

Among other lakes on the north side of the range which offer similar scenery and points of interest, Lake Peter and Lake Schrader are especially to be noted. The former lies at the foot of Mount Chamberlin, second highest peak in the range, which towers nearly 6,000 feet above the shore. Small glaciers cluster around the peak, and one of them terminates only 2,500 feet above the water.

Several lakes on the south side of the range, notably those in the upper part of the Kobuk River Valley, are also of glacial origin, and may be reached easily by float plane. The largest is Walker Lake, about 14 miles long and 1 to 2 miles wide. W. C. Mendenhall, former director of the U.S. Geological Survey, writes of it as follows: "The lake is bordered on both sides by precipitous mountains which rise to heights of 3,000 to 4,000 feet. Southeast of it, toward the mouth of Reed River, the country becomes broken, the hills, which are from 1,000 to 4,000 feet in height, being separated by broad passes, which are often not much above the general level of the streams."

Regarding the origin of the lake, Mendenhall states that the outlet "probably marks approximately the southern limit of the glacier at its principal stage of advance, and the materials discharged at its front, sorted and worn by the waters flowing from it, built up the valley and remained as a dam after the retreat of the ice tongue."

Lakes Selby and Nutuvukti were formed in the same way but are perhaps somewhat less scenic. Lake Takahula is also of glacial origin and, although smaller than those previously mentioned, can be reached by small float plane. Lying as it does midway up the Alatna River, it makes a convenient base for exploratory trips into the heart of the Endicott Mountains. Relatively low passes lead into the Noatak River to the west, the John River to the east, and the Killik and Etivluk rivers to the north, and all four of these rivers head in an area of open mountain meadow along the crest of the range, where there are abundant small lakes, many of which are suitable for small float planes.

Lake Takahula is not only scenic but has an interesting, if somewhat complex, glacial history. P. S. Smith states that "the Alatna basin has undergone extensive glaciation of a valley type, as is shown by many of its topographic features such as truncated spurs, over-steepened slopes, and locally overdeepened valley floors. The whole form of the Alatna Valley shows that it was modeled by a larger and less wieldy agent than running water and then partly filled in and partly reëxcavated, so that the present streams show courses discordant with that of the valley." The Alatna River flows almost entirely through schist and limestone, part of the oldest sequence of rocks in the range.

The Brooks Range by virtue of its arctic setting offers a truly different experience, one compelling prospectors and trappers to remain and drawing explorers back year after year. Here are peaks, ridges, rivers, and lakes to test the skill and endurance of any who seek stimulation in bodily activity; intriguing geologic problems to exercise the mind; and magnificent scenery to please the artistic senses. Here are animals to be hunted and fish to be caught; and a retreat from the pressures of a busy world for those willing to venture far from the well-traveled tourist routes.

GEORGE GRYC

Arctic Slope

Beyond the Brooks Range lies a frozen tundra region that slopes gently to the Arctic Ocean. It is commonly referred to as the Arctic Slope, and although much like tundra regions in Canada and Siberia it is unique under the American flag, and so is of particular interest as a study and testing area and to a more limited extent as a place for recreation.

Except for native villages along the coast and a few military centers, the slope is totally uninhabited. Conspicuous tracks and trails remain, however, as mute reminders of a vast oil exploration program, only recently suspended. These tracks, some of which run for literally hundreds of miles, were made by tractor treads ripping off the thin tundra cover, and they have become deeper and wider by exposing the underlying frozen ground to the summer's sunlight. Interest has lately been revived in the possible commercial development of numerous coal beds, which have been mined for local use at least since the late 1800's; soon caterpillar trains, heavy equipment, and men may return to continue exploration.

The Arctic Slope consists of two distinct geologic and topographic provinces, namely, the Arctic foothills province, which can be divided into the northern and southern foothills sections, and the Arctic coastal plain province.

The Arctic foothills province extends east-west from the Canning River to the vicinity of Cape Lisburne. It lies between the mountainous Brooks Range to the south and the nearly flat Arctic coastal plain to the north. The southern part of the province is characterized by irregular, isolated hills and ridges of sandstone, conglomerate, limestone, and chert that rise above lowlands of shale. The Poko, the Tingmerkpuk, the Fortress, and the Castle Mountains reach altitudes of 3,200, 3,600, 3,625, and 3,726 feet, respectively, but the average elevation is less than 1,000 feet. The northern foothills section of the province is marked by greater topographic regularity, persistent ridges, hills, and mesas having approximately the same altitude.

This contrast in topography is due largely to differences in the character and structure of the rocks underlying the two sections of the foothills province. The southern section shares the structural complexity of the adjacent Brooks Range though it consists of less resistant rocks, including great thicknesses of shale. These rocks, which belong to the Triassic, Jurassic, and early Cretaceous periods, are about 100 to 185 million years old. The northern foothills section, on the other hand, has a less complex structure, consisting primarily of simple folds, and the rocks include massive layers of sandstone and conglomerate that form mesas and hogback ridges, some of which continue for a hundred miles or more. In this section, the rocks range in age from about 75 to 100 million years, all of them belonging to the Cretaceous period.

Beyond the foothills province stretches a vast, monotonous plain marked by thousands of lakes and swamps. This flat region, the Arctic coastal plain province, reflects the simplicity of its underlying structure. The Arctic Slope as a whole marks a great downfold or trough bordered on the south by a complex structural belt that gives way northward to gentle structures along the axis of the trough and then to essentially flat-lying beds under the coastal plain. Hence some of the basement rocks exposed in the Brooks Range plunge under the trough to depths of more than 20,000 feet at Umiat, and then rise gradually to within 2,000 feet of the surface at Barrow.

The geologic history of the Arctic Slope is intimately related to that of the Brooks Range. The oldest known rocks are of late Paleozoic age. At that time, most of the region was a seaway that extended southward over the site of the present Brooks Range. To the north, in the Arctic Ocean north of Siberia and Alaska, lay a large land mass, ancient "Arctica," its southern border lying near Barrow. Throughout late Paleozoic time until the beginning of the Mesozoic era, about 185 million years ago, sediments derived by erosion of "Arctica" were carried by streams into the seaway covering the area now occupied by the Arctic Slope and Brooks Range.

"Arctica" then began to subside, and the southern part of the seaway began to rise until, during the Jurassic period, the ancestral Brooks Range was formed. Repeated uplifts and folding affected the range and to a lesser extent the Arctic Slope throughout the remainder of the Mesozoic era, still further restricting the ancient seaway. Meanwhile, several thousands of feet of sandstone, shale, coal, and other sedimentary deposits accumulated, some containing marine shells and others plant remains. The presence among these sediments of layers of bentonite formed by submarine alteration of ash indicates that volcanoes were active in the region at the beginning of later Cretaceous time, about 80 million years ago.

The region was again uplifted and strongly deformed at the start of the Cenozoic era, but was soon worn to a surface of low relief. Deposits laid down at this time form the conspicuous, gravel-covered White Hills of the Arctic coastal plain province, and fossil plants recovered from them show that sequoia trees then flourished within the Arctic Circle.

Another great uplift, though not involving much folding or faulting, took place about the end of the Tertiary period. Then followed erosion and glaciation. Shortly thereafter, man made his first appearance in North America. In 1947, a Geological Survey party discovered several flint-chipping stations on ridges in the Utukok River area. Among the finds was a Folsom point, indicating the presence of one of the earliest-known human cultures on the continent. Bones, horns, and tusks of fossil mammals are fairly common among the younger rocks of the Arctic Slope, including those of the mammoth, mastodon, buffalo, musk ox, and horse.

We turn now from consideration of the geologic history of the region to brief review of the climate. Nobody would claim that the Arctic Slope provides ideal vacation weather; however, the climate is certainly not one of perpetual snow, ice, and cold. For more than half of the year, the slope is cloaked in almost continuous darkness, and temperatures of 40° and 50° below zero are common. By April, however, the sun reflected from the winter's snows is literally blinding, and by late May in the foothills province only the larger snowbanks remain. Near the coast, snow usually persists until June and is not uncommon throughout the summer. Streams and rivers generally break up during the last two weeks of May, but many lakes, including Lake Schrader and Lake Peter and lakes along the coast, remain frozen well into June or even into early July.

Sunny and reasonably comfortable weather can be expected in the foot-hills province from late May through August. May and June are generally sunny and nearly free of mosquitoes, but by late June and in July the tundra swarms with them, and rainy or cloudy days are common. The total precipitation is not heavy, but the combination of spongy tundra underfoot and low-hanging clouds overhead gives an impression of pervading wetness. And because the ground is permanently frozen below depths of about 2 inches to a foot, surface waters cannot be absorbed.

In the foothills during the summer, temperatures range from the low 40's to the low 80's on exceptionally warm days; then the tundra almost steams. This combination of rain, coolness, and occasional hot days demands a variety of clothing for comfort. A parka-type jacket and reasonably water-proof footgear are particularly recommended. Some type of shoe pack is the most commonly worn footgear. Warm clothes for sudden cold snaps, and lighter clothes for "hot days" and total coverage from mosquitoes, are the main summer requirements. One of the commonest mistakes made by cheechakos is the use of cotton shirts that are too light or too loosely woven to ward off the probing beak of the mosquito. Mosquito repellents are a "must," and headnets can be used for emergencies.

The climate of the Arctic coastal plain is very different. Snow and bitterly cold winds are to be expected even in July. Warm clothing, including a good windbreak garment such as a parka, is essential. Warm and dry foot-gear is also essential and should be selected with care. The coast is generally free from mosquitoes, but an occasional inland wind can soon saturate the air with the pesky insects. Lest the reader think that this discussion has overemphasized unpleasant extremes, it should be added that, in general, the climate is invigorating and not uncomfortable for active work or play.

Camping equipment should also be chosen with care. No matter whether one travels by boat or plane or on foot, lightness is essential. Mosquito-proof tents made of material such as long-fiber cotton are advisable. Portable kerosene or gasoline stoves may be required in the coastal plain where there is almost no wood; along most of the major rivers in the foothills, however, firewood is plentiful.

Those who plan to trip to this remote and little-known region should seek advice from experienced bush pilots or sourdoughs. There are no experi-enced guides except for natives familiar with the coast and generally with the lower reaches of the major rivers, and others at Anaktuvuk Pass, all of whom are familiar with adjacent parts of the Brooks Range and a few of whom are also familiar with part of the foothills province. Several bush pilots are generally familiar with all the Arctic Slope, largely because of the U.S. Navy's oil exploration program, now suspended. One Alaskan airline maintains scheduled flights to Barrow and regular service to other major coastal villages, including Wainwright, Point Lay, and Point Hope.

The flight to Barrow was described in part in the preceding contribution on the Brooks Range. North of the range the flight is generally not very interesting. However, from a large plane on a clear day, or on a ground-contact flight in a bush plane, one can get a good view of the Arctic Slope and observe several topographic and geologic features of interest.

The regular flight is by way of Anaktuvuk Pass. As the plane goes through it to the north side of the Brooks Range, the rugged mountains are seen to give way abruptly to broad, open areas dotted with prominent, isolated peaks. The Anaktuvuk River, which appears immediately below, shows many channels cut into a broad expanse of gravel, the reason being that it has dwindled considerably since the wide river flat was formed during the Pleistocene period when copious meltwaters were supplied by glacial ice.

Once past the front of the Brooks Range, the plane turns toward Gunsight Pass, a water gap flanked by small buckhornlike peaks. The gap, which is conspicuous only from the air and is therefore often used by pilots as a navigational guide, is formed by the Siksikpuk River where it cuts through a prominent escarpment of Cretaceous sandstone. This south-facing escarpment, which can be traced for nearly 200 miles, forms the boundary between the northern and southern foothills sections; it also marks the beginning of the rolling hill country where conspicuous linear ridges reflect broad, open, folded structures beneath the surface.

Upfolds or anticlines are common in oilfields the world over, and it was their presence, coupled with the occurrence of oil seepages, that first called attention to the petroleum possibilities of northern Alaska.

Approximately 20 miles northeast of Gunsight Pass, the plane passes over the Grandstand anticline, not far from where a dry hole was drilled in 1952, to a depth of 3,939 feet, on a terrace on the west bank of the Chandler River. Ahead lie the bluffs along the Colville River, the most conspicuous of which is called Umiat Mountain, although it rises only about 600 feet above the river. This is the site of the Umiat oil field in Naval Petroleum Reserve No. 4, the reserves of which are estimated to be from 30 million to 100 million barrels. The Colville River, which flows past the front of Umiat Mountain, is the largest river in northern Alaska.

A few miles north of Umiat the topography again changes rather abruptly, and thousands of lakes appear. This is the Arctic coastal plain with a relief of no more than a few feet and almost as much water as land. The lakes are particularly interesting because they have regular, generally rectangular outlines, their long axes trending slightly west of north (pl. 23). The reason has not been definitely ascertained, but the lakes may be elongated parallel to the direction of the predominant winds that formerly blew almost at right angles to those of today. Some lakes are now being filled by vegetation; others are being enlarged by erosion of their banks.

The coastal plain is also noteworthy because of the development of polygonal and other geometric patterns in the permanently frozen tundra. Formation of ice wedges has force the ground apart, and where wedges intersect, polygonal patterns have resulted. Some polygons are elevated; others are depressed. Excellent examples of ice wedges are well exposed along the low bluff just upstream from Umiat Mountain and many are exposed along the Colville and other rivers.

Philip S. Smith described the coastal plain as follows:

> Perhaps the most striking characteristic of the coastal plain is the uniformity and monotony of its landscapes. Except for minute minor details, its appearance is everywhere the same. Its slope is so slight that to the unaided eye it appears to stretch away to the horizon as an endless flat. Prominent landmarks are entirely absent. Owing to its featurelessness even minor elevations such as sand dunes 10 feet high appear to be notable prominences; in fact, it is said that one of the earlier explorers reported a range of mountains east of the Colville where subsequent explorations have proved that only low sand dunes exist. Over these plains the winds sweep with unbroken severity, and the traveler caught in the sudden storms that are common in the winter finds it next to impossible to get any natural shelter. In the summer the poorly drained tracts of upland afford only spongy footing, which makes travel laborious and slow, and lakes and deep sloughs necessitate circuitous deviations from direct courses.

All the main northward-flowing rivers that originate in the mountains or foothills reach the ocean. They meander over wide floodplains, and near the coast many of them split into numerous distributaries, emptying into the ocean over broad mud flats too shallow to float even a small canoe.

The flight from Umiat to Barrow crosses at least one major river, the

Ikpikpuk, an Eskimo name meaning "big bank." Near its mouth, the Ikpik-puk splits into two principal channels, the western being called the Chipp River. A broad expanse of lakes and channels makes it almost impossible to follow the main course of the river, part of which flows by devious routes into Admiralty Bay while the main channels empty into Smith Bay. The change from lake and river flats to ocean bay is almost imperceptible.

Point Barrow is a low spit of sand and gravel, about 4 miles long and a quarter of a mile wide. Near its tip, it rises to a height of 15 feet. The spit then turns sharply to the southeast for 2 miles and gives way to a series of small islands that enclose Elson Lagoon, named after the discoverer of Point Barrow. The Barrow airfield and former U.S. Navy facility are on the beach about 5 miles southwest of Point Barrow; the Eskimo village of Bar-row is about 4 miles southwest of the airfield, and the Will Rogers and Wiley Post Memorial is near Walakpai Lagoon about 12 miles southwest of the village.

The Eskimo village is undoubtedly the chief point of interest at Barrow. The visitor landing here for the first time will of course derive pleasure from standing on the beach of the Arctic Ocean. Except for a few weeks during the summer, the polar ice is visible, and throughout much of the year it touches the beach. Shells, jellyfish, and occasional fish are to be seen, and specimens of corals and other forms usually associated with warmer waters are on display in the Arctic Research Laboratory at the former Navy camp.

The shore line of the Arctic is marked nearly everywhere by low cliffs on the mainland and by more or less continuous sand reefs (offshore bars) and islands off the coast. Between the reefs and the mainland are lagoons that, though generally shallow, are deep enough for small boats provided the main channels are known. When the ocean is rough or blocked with ice, the lagoons offer convenient passageways.

The coast has been uplifted during recent geologic time. The shoreward slope of the land is about the same as the submarine slope out to the edge of the continental shelf. In places, wave, ice, and current action has built offshore bars and islands; elsewhere waves beat directly on the mainland, undercutting banks to form cliffs. The shore southeast of Point Barrow il-lustrates the former process; the shore to the southwest illustrates the latter.

Other points of interest are the villages of Wainwright, Point Lay, and Point Hope, all southwest of Barrow. Planes may also be landed at several points east of Point Barrow, but this route is rarely traveled except by mili-tary aircraft. Southwest of Barrow, the coast shows a particularly interesting development of shore features. As far as Wainwright, the mainland is being undercut to form prominent cliffs, and at Skull Cliff, where this action has exposed Cretaceous beds, oil can be seen oozing from the rocks. A few miles southwest of Wainwright, the reef-building process predominates, and reefs continue almost unbroken to several miles beyond Point Lay, the enclosed Kasegaluk Lagoon providing a protected waterway for well over a hundred miles. South and west of Point Lay, where cliff-forming processes again predominate, the rugged coast line exposes rocks of Mesozoic and late Paleozoic age.

Nearly all of the Arctic Slope, including the coast, may be traversed by boat. All the major streams are navigable, although at low water many are too shallow for any but the smallest craft. Seaworthy boats and Eskimo guides are available for hire at Barter Island and Barrow, and probably at Point Lay and Point Hope, if arrangements are made in advance.

The largest and most navigable river is the Colville. One can arrange air transportation to some point in its upper course and then float leisurely the entire length of the river. There are no rapids and only moderately fast water, which can be run with ease. In most places the river is deep enough for a small outboard motor, but there are long, shallow, transverse gravel bars that must be crossed with care. Flash floods are not uncommon, and the water can then rise several feet in a few hours. It is best, therefore, to camp as high as possible. Mosquitoes are a major problem in midsummer, and camp sites should be made on gravel bars away from the swarming tundra.

Several major tributaries of the Colville River, including the Nuka, Etivluk, Killik, Chandler, and Anaktuvuk, are navigable but should be attempted only by those experienced in handling boats in fast and turbulent water. The Killik River is accessible to small float planes by landing on any one of the several lakes near the north front of the Brooks Range. The Chandler River is accessible from Chandler Lake. Although the first 30 miles below the lake are extremely rapid and turbulent, it was traversed successfully by a Geological Survey boat party in 1945. The Anaktuvuk River, accessible by landing on Tulugak Lake in the Brooks Range, is, however, shallow and extremely braided in low water.

In addition to the Colville River system, several other major rivers of the Arctic Slope, such as the Kuparuk, Sagavanirktok, and Canning, are traversable with reasonable facility. The Canning River is particularly spectacular as it flows for 20 miles along the western end of the Shublik and the Sadlerochit Mountains. It is accessible by bush plane, but only one or two pilots are intimately familiar with the area. The extreme western part of the

Arctic Slope is drained by three navigable rivers, the Utukok, Kokolik, and Kuparuk. These rivers cross a foothills area more spectacular in many respects than the area along the Colville River. Prominent sandstone ridges form racecourselike outlines around geologic structures.

A traverse of any of the rivers mentioned provides an excellent opportunity to observe the wild life, topography, and geology of the Arctic Slope. In late summer, one may cross the path of a herd of migrating caribou. Such herds, numbering in the thousands, begin to gather in July, and have been seen in the Colville River area every summer from 1945 through 1953. Moose have apparently become more plentiful in recent years, especially along the Colville River, where the author counted twelve in a distance of about 30 miles.

Although the Arctic Slope is essentially treeless, willows, averaging 3 to 6 feet in height and 1 to 2 inches in diameter, are common along all the major rivers; indeed, some willows reach 20 to 25 feet in height and measure 5 to 6 inches across. On many of the major rivers, particularly the Chandler, Anaktuvuk, Canning, Echooka, and Kongakut, there are groves of poplars up to 40 feet high and 8 inches in diameter. Except for scrub juniper, evergreens appear to be absent.

The bedrocks of the Arctic Slope are best studied in cutbank exposures along streams and rivers, but the mantle of Pleistocene glacial deposits and lush tundra vegetation elsewhere make this a poor region for geological examination. Enough can be seen, however, to give a general idea of the formations and structure of the region. Particularly noteworthy are the bluffs along the Colville River from Umiat downstream to Ocean Point, in which bedrock is almost continuously exposed for a distance of about 50 miles. All of the rocks are of Cretaceous age, dating back about 75 million years. Oil seepages can be seen near the base of Umiat Mountain, both on the river and in lakes and ponds just west of the mountain, and fossil shells can be collected at Umiat Mountain and in the next large bluff downstream from Umiat.

Thus the Arctic Slope, despite its limited access, offers many recreational possibilities. A flight across this almost treeless, tundra wasteland, or a trip by boat down one of its many navigable rivers, provides an experience never to be forgotten.

GEORGE M. FLINT, JR.

Islands of the Bering Sea

The 100-fathom line runs northwest from near the southern tip of Umnak Island to the Siberian coast. To the northeast, following a much more irregular though roughly parallel course, runs the 40-fathom line. These lines reflect the northeastward shoaling of the Bering Sea. Essentially the only islands within the sea, save for the Aleutian Islands, which form its southern boundary, lie within the shallow confines of the 40-fathom line.

The islands that break the broad expanse of the Bering Sea range in size from diminutive Sledge Island, a mile and a half long, to St. Lawrence Island with a maximum length of 110 miles. Several islands, though seldom visited by the casual tourist, are significant to Alaska's economy and tradition, and all provide keys to a better understanding of its geologic history.

The present chapter is concerned only with the largest islands, namely, St. Lawrence, St. Matthew, the Pribilofs, Nelson, and Nunivak. Some of the other islands, such as Bogoslof and the small islands along the north edge of the Aleutian arc, have been referred to in an earlier contribution; still other islands are too little known geologically to be the subject of separate discussion. These include Little Diomede, less than 3 miles to the west but the property of the USSR, and King Island, noted for its settlement of Eskimo fishermen and ivory craftsmen who traditionally display their wares along the beach at Nome during the summer months.

ST. LAWRENCE ISLAND

St. Lawrence Island, in the northern part of the Bering Sea, lies 124 miles southwest of the Seward Peninsula and only 42 miles east of Siberia. It was first sighted by the Russian explorer Vitus Bering on St. Lawrence's Day, August 10, 1728, when, sailing through Bering Strait, he discovered that the land east of Siberia was not a part of Asia. Aside from missionary activities, however, the island remained essentially unvisited by whites until recent years. Only whalers and chance voyagers, tired by the buffeting of the northern seas, sought shelter in the lee of the island. They bartered for curios and found relaxation among the natives, many of whom are related by blood to the Siberian Eskimos.

In 1878 it was estimated that 3,000 people, chiefly Eskimos, lived in ten villages around the shores, subsisting on seals, walrus, whales, and water birds. Three years later, the population had fallen to about five hundred, most of the inhabitants having died of starvation and disease during the winter of 1878–79. The native population has never increased markedly above this figure, and today many of the older settlements are no more than archaeological sites. About 80 per cent of the population live in Gambell and Savoogna; the rest are scattered over the island. Temporary camps are established during the summer and fall for gathering food plants, hunting seal and walrus, and trapping fox.

Ice breakers have been operated to Savoogna and Gambell in midwinter, but the island is surrounded by the arctic ice pack for eight months of the year, and commercial navigation is limited to the remaining summer months. The weather is cold, windy, and humid. Total precipitation is not high, but freezing rain and snow have been reported every month of the year, and fogs are common, especially during the summer.

There are no trees or shrubs of any height, and the natives frequently use driftwood for lumber. Moss, lichens, grasses, creeping willows and birches, and other kinds of tundra vegetation cover the entire island, and during the summer the cold, dreary-looking landscape is brightened by many varieties of colorful flowers, including larkspurs, saxifrages, anemones, and daisies that form luxuriant gardens.

Near the center of the island is the so-called "Kookooligit volcanic upland," including Mount Atuk, the highest point, with an altitude of 2,070 feet. Much of the southwest end of the island and parts of the east end compose the "crystalline uplands," ranging up to 1,700 feet, but predominantly

800 to 1,000 feet in altitude. Most of the remaining two-thirds of the island is low-lying and nearly featureless, and much of it is covered by tundra and dotted with hundreds of small lakes.

The lowlands are underlain generally by sedimentary and metamorphic rocks, some of which contain fossils that indicate a probable Devonian or Carboniferous age. Granitic masses of late Mesozoic and early Cenozoic age intrude these rocks, forming mountain groups and isolated peaks that rise abruptly from the tundra. The north-central part of the island is blanketed by Tertiary and perhaps by Recent volcanic rocks. Here are to be seen fresh, steep-sided cinder cones and jagged flows of lava. Several flows cross raised beaches, and the youngest exhibit such well-preserved features as to suggest effusion in very recent time.

St. Lawrence Island, unlike other islands in the Bering Sea, has a geologic history that goes back to late Paleozoic time, when the area lay beneath a warm, shallow sea in which thick limestones were deposited. Earth movements then took place, accompanied by extrusion of volcanic rocks on what is now the eastern third of the island. Deposition of sediments continued during the Triassic (?) period, but by Jurassic and Cretaceous times the dominant activity was widespread volcanism and intrusion of plutonic masses that metamorphosed the older rocks.

Tertiary time was one of continued accumulation of gravels, sands, and clays, and of extensive volcanic activity near the center of the island. It was then also that the island was partly submerged, permitting the sea to carve the highest terraces. Volcanoes continued to erupt during Quaternary time, becoming increasingly localized near the highest part of the Kookooligit Mountains. Oscillation of the sea level has ended, for the moment, in a general uplift.

Little attention has been paid to the potential mineral resources of the island, except for scattered unsuccessful prospecting. None of the lands have been subject to location, settlement, sale, or entry, because they are classified by Presidential order as a "reindeer station"; hence private development has been limited to sporadic efforts of the natives.

Known coal resources consist of seams of Tertiary lignite and locally subbituminous coal varying from a few inches to 2 or more feet in thickness. These occur at several localities in the lowlands. Pyrite, galena, sphalerite, and molybdenite have been found in the southwest part of the island but no economically significant deposits have yet been recognized.

Visitors approaching Savoonga from the east first sight the prominent seastacks known as the Stolby Rocks, located 2 miles offshore. They tower some 160 feet above the sea, and from certain directions resemble a ship on the horizon. Close inspection of the island from the air reveals large expanses of rough lava, boulder fields caused by intense frost action, and fields of stone nets that merge into stone stripes on gentle hill slopes.

Perhaps the most spectacular and unusual features of the island are the triangular or cuspate deposits that jut from the barrier beaches and mainland into the protected lagoons along the south side. Nearly twenty such spits, from 350 to 3,200 feet in base-to-apex length, have been observed, and many of them form slightly offset pairs, one extending from the mainland and the other from a barrier beach. Among the long enduring memories carried away by the visitor to St. Lawrence Island will certainly be the sight of these spits whitely outlined against the cold, dark waters of the Bering Sea.

ST. MATTHEW ISLAND

St. Matthew and adjoining islands are surrounded by an ice pack for much of the year, and are covered during most of the short navigation season with the dense fog so typical around the islands of the Bering Sea. Not being endowed with such natural resources as the fur seals of the Pribilofs, and having few sheltered sections of coast line suitable as fishing bases for natives, St. Matthew and adjacent Hall and Pinnacle islands have remained uninhabited. Early visitors to St. Matthew reported seeing many polar bears along the shore, but there is no recent information about them.

The island lies about 135 miles west of Nunivak. It measures about 33 miles long and averages 4 miles across. From a distance it appears to consist of ten or twelve separate masses, but actually these are connected by low spits of sand and gravel. They are said to be made up of tough, compact, platy andesitic lava, each rising 900 to 1,500 feet above the sea. No distinct craters have been recognized, nor are there any recent lavas, like those on the Pribilofs.

The highest points on St. Matthew Island are bare; areas of intermediate height are covered with swampy moss and grass, and lowland areas are mainly tundra. There are no harbors, but where lowlands come down to the sea there are beaches and landing places.

Hall Island, 3 miles to the northwest of St. Matthew, includes the highest peak in the group, with an elevation of 1,665 feet. Rugged cliffs surround the island, and its top is covered with rocky moss.

Eight miles south of St. Matthew and connected to it by a narrow submerged ridge is inaccessible Pinnacle Island. This is less than 2 miles long, and its striking spires and needlelike formations rise abruptly from the sea to a height of 1,250 feet.

PRIBILOF ISLANDS

The Pribilofs lie on the 170th meridian, some 200 miles northwest of Unalaska. They were known to the native Aleuts long before the first white men visited them. On June 12, 1786, the Russian explorer Gavrilo Pribilof landed on St. George Island, but not until a year later, on a second visit, did he sight St. Paul, the largest island of the group. The two islands are only 40 miles apart, yet the prevailing fog had obscured St. Paul during Pribilof's earlier visit.

Pribilof Islands is the name now generally applied to the five islands of the group. The Aleuts called them "Amig." The largest islands—St. Paul, about 35 square miles, and St. George, about 27 square miles—are the only two that are inhabited. The three much smaller islands are Otter, Walrus, and Sealion Rock; the two last rise only a few feet above sea level, and in stormy weather breakers wash over them.

There are no harbors on either St. Paul or St. George, and navigation around them is dangerous. Thick fog envelops the islands for nine days out of ten in the summer months, and unless the wind is directly offshore there is no good anchorage. The islands, moreover, are at the southern limit of ice in the Bering Sea, and detached ice is generally present in their vicinity from February to May.

St. George consists mainly of rugged hills and ridges, and the entire coast, except for several short stretches, is a precipitous cliff that at one point reaches a height of 984 feet. The west and southwest parts of St. Paul are high and rugged, with steep cliffs along the coast. Bogoslof Hill, which rises near this end of the island, reaches an altitude of 590 feet. Apart from scattered rocky areas and local bluffs, the shore line in this part of the island is a sandy beach. The remainder of the island is a comparatively low, rolling plateau dotted with extinct volcanic peaks.

A vivid green coat of moss and grasses covers the Pribilof Islands during summer, contrasting sharply with colored plants and flowering annuals. So diversified is the flora that amateur botanists on St. Paul have found more than 120 different specimens in a single day's collecting. The dry windy winters have an average temperature of 22° to 26° above zero; the range during the foggy wet summers is 46° to 50° F.

Several hundred natives live on St. Paul and St. George islands, most of them being descendants of Aleutian Islanders imported by the Russians to assist in the seal hunts. Besides these natives, now largely of mixed Russian-Aleut blood, there are a few white residents who supervise the fur-seal industry and provide community facilities to the natives.

The key to the economy of the islands is the world-famous fur-seal reservation. For centuries seals have come to these islands to breed, and hunters have killed them for their furs. Yet despite the vigorous operations of the Russians there were still several million seals when Alaska was purchased in 1867. Uncontrolled taking of furs during the next two generations brought the animals perilously close to extinction. Now, thanks to attempts at international regulation begun in 1911, the herd is again in a healthy condition.

Today, seal killing is carried on by the U.S. Fish and Wildlife Service, and each year a census of the herd is taken and surplus males of a certain age-group are selected for killing. During the summer months, the Pribilof beaches become rookeries alive with countless thousands of harems, each composed of a bull with his cows and pups, surrounded by the bachelors, and from the entire area rise hoarse, sibilant whistles audible 6 miles away and a curious unpleasant odor detectable from just as far. Herds of arctic foxes, which are trapped during the winter months, provide the only supplemental source of income. In the spring and early summer the natives, at great risk, collect boatloads of eggs of the guillemot and other sea birds that nest on Otter and Walrus islands.

The Pribilofs are composed dominantly of basaltic lava flows and intrusive sills. Fragmental products of explosive eruptions, and glacial sediments, are present in minor amount. The lavas must be quite recent, for some are interbedded with glacial sediments and others overlie them. About thirty species of marine fossils have been identified from these youthful glacial deposits. The oldest rock on the islands is a peridotite that forms a glaciated basement on St. George, and locally fossil shells, no older than Pleistocene, are "glued" directly upon it.

The Pribilofs seem to have been built by copious fissure eruptions during Pleistocene time. Their average elevation was probably high during the early part of the period, but since then there has been a general subsidence accompanied by fissuring, faulting, and outpouring of lava. Some flows have smooth surfaces clothed with a thin layer of moss and grasses; others are very sparingly overgrown and have highly uneven surfaces marked by wavelike corrugations, spongy scoria, and foam. Indeed these young flows

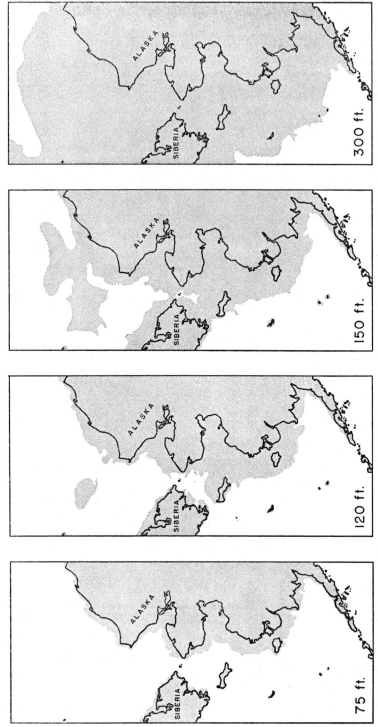

Figure 3. Development of the Bering Sea Land Bridge. Diagrams to show expansion of land areas when sea level sank 75, 120, 150, and 300 feet during the Pleistocene period. (Prepared by D. M. Hopkins.)

are so well preserved that they seem just to have solidified. On St. Paul Island, between Fox Hill and the west coast, one rather extensive flow exhibits a magnificent display of miniature volcanic forms, including a multitude of hornitos, once gas-emitting vents, as well as chimneys formed by lava spatter, blow holes, and tiny craters. Cones, such as Bogoslof, are also prominent on the island.

Little study has yet been made of the interbedded Pleistocene sediments, but there can be no doubt that systematic examination will yield information of much importance. It may, for instance, unravel details concerning glaciation and movements of the land relative to sea level, and serve to correlate such movements with times of volcanic eruption.

NELSON ISLAND

Nelson Island is separated from the lowland plains of the Yukon-Kuskokwim delta by two riverlike channels that connect Baird Inlet to the Bering Sea. The scenery and geology of the island are dominated by the cliffs of Cape Vancouver, almost 1,000 feet high, and by other precipitous headlands.

Folded carbonaceous sedimentary rocks of Cretaceous age crop out along the beaches on the seaward side of the island. Here the natives pick up many rock fragments showing well-preserved impressions of plants that flourished more than 60 million years ago, and occasionally small bits of amber (fossil resin) are recovered from wave-washed rubble on the beach.

Benches or mesalike remnants of nearly flat-lying basaltic lava flows, similar to those on Nunivak Island, form the topmost parts of the western cliffs and almost all of the eastern highland area. Red and yellow iron oxides produced by weathering of these rocks have been used as decorative pigments and formerly were items of barter among the Alaskan natives.

Vegetation on Nelson Island is limited to small tundra plants and mosses, and to a few stunted willows and alders in protected spots along some of the streams. Driftwood washed on to the beaches—probably from the Kuskokwim River drainage and the Bristol Bay area—is used for fuel and occasionally for construction.

NUNIVAK ISLAND

Nunivak Island, lying astride the 60th parallel and separated by the shallow Etolin Strait from Nelson Island and the lowland plains of western Alaska, is another Bering Sea island of volcanic origin. Most of it consists of gentle slopes that descend from a few scattered, sharp peaks marking the sites of late Tertiary or Quaternary volcanic vents. The center of the island is dominated by Roberts Mountain, a volcanic peak 1,675 feet high, with a breached crater at the top.

The bluffs forming most of the coast line vary in height from a few feet to more than 450 feet. They consist of volcanic rocks, many of which are markedly columnar. Small embayments usually have narrow sand or gravel beaches. Near the larger bays and at Cape Etolin enough sand has accumulated to form sizable dunes, now more or less stabilized by a light cover of vegetation.

Weathering of basaltic bedrocks produces fertile soils in favorable regions, but the rigorous Bering Sea climate limits both soil formation and vegetation, so that the islands are essentially barren except for the usual tundra association of small plants and mosses. Only in protected areas along some of the streams are there a few stunted willows and alders.

The presence of abundant tundra range of good quality has contributed materially to the successful introduction of reindeer and musk ox into the Nunivak National Wildlife Refuge. In 1954, the musk ox herd contained between ninety-four and a hundred animals, and it is slowly increasing. The reindeer herd, safe from the foraging wolves of the mainland, is controlled to the range limitation by systematic annual harvesting of surplus animals in a colorful roundup.

Geologic Time Scale

Era	Period	Approximate number of years ago (in millions)
Cenozoic	Pleistocene (Ice Age)	1
	Pliocene	1 to 10
	Miocene	10 to 30
	Oligocene	30 to 40
	Eocene	40 to 60
Mesozoic	Cretaceous	60 to 130
	Jurassic	130 to 155
	Triassic	155 to 185
Paleozoic	Permian	185 to 210
	Pennsylvanian & Mississippian	210 to 265
	Devonian	265 to 320
	Silurian	320 to 360
	Ordovician	360 to 440
	Cambrian	440 to 520
Proterozoic	Precambrian	520 to 2,500+

Glossary

Acidic rocks. Igneous rocks with more than 66 per cent silica; most of them contain quartz.

Andesite. A volcanic rock composed essentially of soda-lime feldspar (plagioclase) and one or more dark minerals, such as biotite, hornblende, augite, and hypersthene.

Anticline. An upfold or arch.

Argillite. Firmly indurated sedimentary rock originally composed chiefly of clay. It is less clearly laminated than shale; its formation usually involves some recrystallization of the parent sediment; in short, it is a weakly metamorphosed mudstone.

Ash. The finest product of explosive volcanic eruptions. The particles measure less than 4 millimeters across and may consist of glass or crystalline material.

Augite. A dark silicate mineral of variable composition but containing iron, magnesia, alumina, and lime.

Basalt. The most abundant of all volcanic rocks. Usually dark in color and with 45 to 52 per cent silica. Its chief minerals are lime-rich feldspar, olivine, augite, and magnetite.

Batholith. A large igneous intrusion generally found in the cores of fold-mountain ranges. Most batholiths consist of granite or some closely allied, coarse-grained rock developed either by slow cooling and crystallization of material that was originally molten, or by alteration of preëxisting rocks under the influence of high temperatures and pressures and permeating solutions.

Biotite. Dark mica. A flaky, flexible silicate mineral containing iron, magnesia, potash, and alumina.

Breccia, volcanic. Fragmental product of explosive volcanic eruptions. The constituent fragments are angular, and most of them exceed 32 millimeters in diameter.

Cassiterite. Tin oxide; the chief source of tin.

Chert. A compact, more or less pure siliceous rock composed of opal, chalcedony, or minutely crystalline quartz. It is usually a marine or fresh-water sedimentary rock that is formed either by chemical precipitation of silica or by accumulation of the remains of siliceous organisms, such as diatoms and radiolaria.

Cirque. An amphitheater- or armchair-like valley head produced by glacial erosion.

Conglomerate. A sedimentary rock consisting chiefly of rounded pebbles, cobbles, and boulders; a consolidated gravel.

Diabase. The intrusive equivalent of basalt. Most dark dikes and sills consist of this rock.

Dike. A more or less parallel-sided wall of igneous rock formed by solidification of molten material injected into a fissure that cuts across the layering of the adjacent rocks.

Diorite. A coarse-grained igneous rock composed chiefly of soda-lime feldspar and such dark minerals as biotite and hornblende; quartz may or may not be present.

Dolomite. A mineral or sedimentary rock composed of lime-magnesium carbonate.

Feldspar. The commonest of all silicate minerals. The chief potash-rich variety is *orthoclase;* varieties rich in soda or lime or both are called *plagioclase.*

Galena. Lead sulfide; the main ore of lead.

Geanticline. A major upfold or anticline in the earth's crust.

Geosyncline. A major trough, usually submarine, in which thick deposits of sedimentary and volcanic rocks accumulate during long, slow subsidence of the floor.

Gneiss. A metamorphic rock marked by coarse texture and irregular banding. It does not split readily because of the preponderance of quartz and feldspar over micas.

Granite. A coarse-grained igneous rock composed of quartz and with more potash feldspar than soda-lime feldspar. The principal dark minerals are usually biotite and hornblende.

Granodiorite. A coarse-grained igneous rock not unlike granite but one in which potash feldspar forms between a third and an eighth of all the feldspar.

Graywacke. A dark, firmly indurated sandstone with a partly recrystallized matrix of clay. Many graywackes contain dark rock fragments, such as slate, most of which, like the individual mineral grains, are angular and quite variable in size. Graywackes generally accumulate rapidly in geosynclines.

Greenstone. Altered basaltic lava or diabase. Most greenstone in Alaska was formed from submarine lava and is interbedded with sedimentary rocks.

Hornblende. A greenish silicate mineral similar to augite in composition except for the presence of a little hydroxyl.

Hypersthene. A dark, iron-magnesium silicate mineral differing from augite in the absence of lime and alumina.

Igneous rock. A rock formed by cooling and solidification of hot, mobile rock matter made up wholly, or in appreciable part, of a liquid having the composition of a silicate melt. Lava is an extrusive variety, and granite is a deep-seated, intrusive variety.

Kettle lake. A lake occupying a basin in glacial deposits. It is made by melting of an isolated mass of buried ice.

Marble. A metamorphic rock formed by recrystallization of limestone.

Metamorphic rock. A rock altered while solid by recrystallization and reaction between the component minerals. The changes result from heat, pressure, and chemically active fluids.

Mica. A flaky, flexible mineral. The chief colorless variety, *muscovite,* is a potash-aluminum silicate with hydroxyl; the chief dark variety, *biotite,* contains iron and magnesia as well.

Monzonite. A coarse-grained igneous rock in which potash feldspar and soda-lime feldspar are present in approximately equal quantities. Quartz may or may not be present, and the typical dark mineral is hornblende.

Obsidian. Volcanic glass, usually having the composition of andesite or rhyolite or of some lava intermediate between these two.

Olivine. An iron-magnesium silicate mineral.

Orthoclase. Potash feldspar.

Peridotite. An ultrabasic rock, generally green, composed mainly of olivine and augite; often altered to serpentine.

Permafrost. See pages 36 and 78–81.

Phyllite. A fine-grained metamorphic rock that splits easily and has a lustrous sheen owing to the presence of abundant, finely divided white mica.

Plagioclase. Soda-lime feldspar.

Plutonic rock. A coarse-grained igneous rock that crystallized slowly deep beneath the surface. Batholiths consist of such rocks.

Quartz. The commonest of all minerals; composed of silica.

Quartzite. Hard, sugary-textured metamorphic rock derived from quartz sandstone. The original quartz grains have recrystallized into an interlocking mosaic. Quartzite generally breaks across the grains, not around them as do most sandstones.

Rhyolite. An acid, i.e., silica-rich volcanic rock usually containing visible crystals of quartz, feldspar, and biotite. The matrix may be glassy or very finely crystalline.

Scheelite. Lime tungstate.

Schist. A metamorphic rock characterized by subparallel arrangement of abundant flaky minerals, such as micas, or of fibrous and blady minerals, such as hornblende. A common feature of a schist is that it splits easily into thin sheets that are mineralogically similar.

Schistosity. The property of a metamorphic rock whereby it can be split into thin flakes or lenticles.

Shale. A laminated sedimentary rock derived from mud and composed chiefly of clay minerals most of which lie parallel to the lamination so that the rock splits with ease.

Sill. A tabular sheet of igneous rock injected along the bedding planes of sedimentary or volcanic rocks.

Slate. Very fine-grained metamorphic rock that splits readily into thin sheets. The cleavage surfaces, unlike those of phyllite, are dull rather than lustrous. Most slate is derived from shale or tuff.

Solifluction. See page 83.

Sphalerite. Zinc sulfide.

Stibnite. Antimony sulfide.

Syncline. A downfold in rocks.

Synclinorium. A major downfold in the earth's crust which includes subordinate synclines and anticlines.

Till. Hummocky debris left by glaciers and marked by a heterogeneous, unstratified mixture of boulders, sand, and clay.

Tuff. Compacted volcanic ash.

Ultrabasic rock. A dark igneous rock with a silica percentage of less than 45, consisting chiefly of olivine and augite. Many such rocks are altered by hydration to greenish serpentine.

Index of
Geographical Names

Admiralty: Bay, 125; Island, 10, 11, 18
Agiapuk River, 106
Ahklune Mountains, 51, 84
Akutan volcano, 63, 68
Alaska, Gulf of, 3, 5, 6, 12, 17, 19–29, 38
Alaska Highway, 79, 80, 91, 101, 102
Alaska Peninsula, 6, 7, 8, 61–75
Alaska Railroad, 22, 24, 26, 38, 49, 50, 51, 52, 56, 57, 58, 60
Alaska Range, 3, 5, 6, 11, 19, 20, 21, 30, 33, 34, 38, 43, 44, 45, 46, 47, 48–60, 76, 80, 84
Alatna River, 14, 115, 117, 118
Aleutian: Islands, 8, 29, 61–75, 128; Range, 3, 6, 7, 48, 61, 63, 75; volcanoes, 63, 64–67
Alexander Archipelago, 9, 18
Alsek River, 23, 27
American Creek, 102
Anakserak River, 114
Anaktuvuk Pass, 114, 115, 116, 122, 123; River, 114, 115, 116, 123, 126, 127
Anchorage, 34, 50, 54, 61
Anderson Pass, 51, 54

Aniak, 83, 86
Aniakchak caldera, 68
Aniuk River, 114, 115
Annette Island, 10, 14
Antarctica, 6, 13
Anvil Creek, 110
Arctic, 96; Circle, 7, 105, 111, 121; coastal plain province, 119–122, 124; foothills province, 119, 120; Research Laboratory, 125; Slope, 4, 5, 6, 7, 99, 119–127
"Arctica," 120, 121
Attu Island, 61
Auke Lake, 17

Bagley Ice Field, 22, 24
Baird: Inlet, 134; Mountains, 112
Banner Creek, 101
Baranof Island, 10, 11, 12, 14, 18
Barometer Mountain, 87
Barrow, 6, 99, 114, 120, 124, 125, 126. See also Point Barrow
Barter Island, 126

Beardslee Islands, 16
Beaver: Creek, 49, 92, 97, 99; Mountains, 83
Bendeleben Mountains, 105, 106
Bering: Glacier, 25, 28; River, 28
Bethel, 86
Bettles, 100, 115
Big Delta, 101
Big Hurrah Mine, 106
Birch Creek, 55, 60, 92, 95, 99, 100, 101, 102
Black Rapids: Glacier, 52, 57; Lodge, 53
Black River, 94
Bogoslof Hill, 132, 135; Island, 73, 128; volcano, 73, 75
Bohemia Basin, 17
Bonnifield mining district, 52
Brady Glacier, 17
Bristol Bay, 51, 82, 84, 86; area, 134
British Mountains, 112
Brooks Range, 3–7 *passim*, 53, 76, 84, 88, 95, 96, 99, 100, 111–118, 119, 120, 122
Buldir Island, 63; "Buldir depression," 63

Camp Eielson, 58
Canning River, 112, 115, 120, 126, 127
Canwell Glacier, 53
Cantwell, 34; formation, 5, 58
Cape Darby, 105
Cape Espenberg, 105, 106
Cape Etolin, 136
Cape Fairweather, 24, 28
Cape Lisburne, 120
Cape Prince of Wales, 105, 106
Cape St. Elias, 24
Cape Suckling, 28
Cape Vancouver, 135
Cape Wooley, 106
Cape York, 105
Capps Glacier, 50
Carlisle volcano, 63
Caro, 96
Castle Rock (Old Bogoslof), 74, 75
Castle Mountains, 120
Castner Glacier, 53
Central, 101
Cerberus (volcanic cone), 68
Chakachatna River, 50
Chandalar: Lake, 114; mines, 95; River, 95, 96, 97, 114, 115
Chandler: Lake, 114, 126; River, 114, 115, 123, 126, 127
Charley River, 92
Chatanika, 101; River, 99, 100, 101
Chatham Strait, 11, 12, 16, 18
Cheenik, 104
Chena River, 89, 92, 97

Chickaloon River, 41
Chichagof, 10, 17; Island, 10, 11, 12, 14, 17
Chicken, 92, 102
Chimney Mountain, 32
Chipp River, 125
Chisana: area, 32; River, 49, 53, 79
Chistochina, 30
Chitina: 24, 35, 37; River, 31; Valley, 19, 32
Chitistone River, 32
Christmas Mountain, 85
Chugach Mountains, 6, 19–25 *passim*, 27, 30, 33, 34, 38, 44–46 *passim*
Chugach-Kenai: provinces, 19; range, 19, 38
Chugach-Kenai-Kodiak mountain chain, 3, 5, 23, 26
Chugach–St. Elias mountain chain, 25, 27
Chuilnuk Mountains, 83
Chukchi Sea, 105
Circle, 91, 92, 97, 99, 101; Hot Springs, 92, 97, 99, 101
Clarence: Glacier, 15; Strait, 14
Cleveland volcano, 63
Coleen River, 94, 95, 114, 115
Coast Range, 4, 5, 6, 9–13 *passim*, 15–20 *passim*
Colville River, 114, 115, 123, 124, 126, 127
Columbia River plateau, 56
Controller Bay, 28
Cook Inlet, 19, 43, 44, 46, 47, 49, 50; –Susitna Lowland, 5, 43–47
Copper: Center, 30; Glacier, 46; River, 19, 22, 23, 24, 26, 28, 31, 34, 36, 37, 46, 49; plateau, 30, 34–37, 38, 46, 56
Copper River and Northwestern Railroad, 24
Cordova, 23, 26
Council, 106, 107
Crazy Mountains, 92, 101
Crooked Creek, 83
Cross Sound, 19
Curry, 51; Lookout, 51

Darby Mountains, 105, 106, 107
Davidson: Ditch, 101; Mountains, 111, 112
Dawson, 102
DeCourcy Mountain, 87; Mine, 87
DeLong Mountains, 112, 114
Delta: Glacier, 60; River, 46, 49, 52, 53; Valley, 52, 80
Denali Highway, 38
Dennison Fork, 102; West Fork of, 102
Devil Mountain, 106
Disenchantment Bay, 21
Dixon Entrance, 9
Donnelly Dome, 60
Douglas Island, 16
Dry Bay, 21, 23

Eagle, 102; trail, 50; -Valdez trail, 53
Echooka River, 127
Edgerton Cutoff, 34
Elephant Mountain, 93
Elliott Highway, 91
Elson Lagoon, 125
Endicott, 10; Mountains, 112, 114, 117
Engineer Creek, 100
Ernestine, 26
Ester, 80
Etivluk River, 115, 117, 126
Etolin: Island, 11; Strait, 134
Eureka, 35, 92

Fairbanks, 54, 80–81, 91, 98, 99, 100, 101, 115; area, 95, 97
Fairweather Range, 14, 16, 20
Faith Creek, 101
Farewell Landing Field, 50
Feniak Lake, 114
Fire Island, 7
Firth River, 114
Fish River, 106
Flat, 85, 87; Creek, 85
Fort Yukon, 98, 99, 115
Fortress Mountains, 120
Fortymile: area, 98, 102; gold camp, 91; River, 92, 97, 102; Roadhouse, 102
Four Mountains, 63
Fox, 100, 101; Hill, 135
Franklin: Creek, 102; Mountains, 112
Frederick Sound, 18
Frederika: Glacier, 31; Valley, 32

Gakona, 30
Galena, 99
Gambell, 129
Gareloi: Island, 63; volcano, 63
Gastineau Channel, 15–18 *passim*
Glacier: Bay, 10, 11, 12, 16; Creek, 110; Highway, 17; National Monument, 16
Glenn Highway, 34, 35, 38, 42, 50, 53
Globe Creek, 100
Gold Creek, 15
"Golden Heart of Alaska," 88
Golovnin Bay, 104, 105
Goodnews: Bay, 86; Glacier, 84; Lake, 85; River, 84
Goodpaster River, 89, 92, 97, 98
Grandstand anticline, 123
Grantley Harbor, 105
Gravina Island, 14
Great Sitkin caldera, 68
Grewingk, 74
Gulkana, 34; Glacier, 53
Gunsight Pass, 123

Gustavus airport, 10, 16
Guyot Glacier, 25, 29

Hall Island, 131
Harding: Ice Field, 22; Lake, 101
Hasselborg Lake, 18
Haycock, 106; –Peace River area, 107
Healy, 52, 58; Creek, 59
Hess Mountain, 52
Highway Pass, 56
Hinchinbrook Island, 28
Hirst-Chichagof, 17
Holitna River, 87
Holy Cross, 86
Horn Mountains, 83
Hot Springs Dome, 93
Howard: Lake, 114; Pass, 114
Hughes, 89, 90
Hulahula River, 115
Hunt Fork, 115
Hurricane, 51
Hutlinana, 103

Icy: Bay, 21, 25, 28, 29; Point, 19, 21, 24, 28; Strait, 16, 17
Iditarod, 85, 87; River, 86
Ikpikpuk River, 125
Imuruk Lake, 106, 109
Indian Mountain, 90
Inian Islands, 17
Innoko River, 86
"Inside Passage," 7, 9, 14
Ipnavik River, 115
Iron Creek, 41
Itkillik River, 115

Jago River, 115
Joe Creek, 116
John River, 14–117 *passim*
Jumbo Dome, 58
Juneau, 10, 14, 16, 17, 18

Kachemak Bay, 43, 44
Kahiltna Glacier, 50
Kanaga: Island, 63; volcano, 63, 68
Kanak Island, 28
Kanaton caldera, 68
Kandik River, 93
Kanektok River, 84
Kantishna Hills, 51, 52, 55; mining district, 52
Kanuti River, 91
Kasegaluk Lagoon, 126
Kashwitna River, 41, 44, 47
Katalla district, 25
Katmai: caldera, 69, 70, 71; Pass, 69; village, 69. *See also* Mount Katmai

Kenai: lowland, 19, 47; Mountains, 19, 21, 22, 23, 24, 27, 28, 43, 46; Peninsula, 21–22, 43. *See also* Chugach-Kenai; Chugach-Kenai-Kodiak mountain chain
Kennicott mines, 23, 31, 32, 33
Ketchikan, 10, 14
Kigluaik (Sawtooth) Mountains, 105, 106, 110
Kilbuck Mountains, 84
Kiligwa River, 115
Killik River, 112, 114, 115, 117, 126
King Island, 128
King Salmon, 71
Kiokluk Mountains, 83
Kiska Island, 63
Klondike, 9, 30, 49
Klutina River, 36
Knik: Arm, 43, 46; River, 44
Kobuk River, 82; Valley, 117
Kodiak, 26; Island, 19, 23, 26; Mountains, 19, 23, 24, 27, 28
Kokolik River, 127
Kokrine Hills, 91, 99
Kongakut River, 114, 115, 127
Kookooligit Mountains, 130; "Kookooligit volcanic upland," 129
Kootznahoo Inlet, 18
Kotzebue, 99, 115; Sound, 82, 106, 115
Kougarok placer district, 109
Koyuk, 106; River, 106
Koyukuk: geosyncline, 4; mining region, 100; River, 88, 89, 90, 99, 115
Kruzof Island, 14
Kugruk River, 107
Kugurorok River, 114, 115
Kuiu Island, 10, 11, 12
Kulukak River, 84
Kuparuk River, 126, 127
Kupreanof Island, 10, 11
Kurupa: Lake, 114; River, 114
Kuskokwim: highlands, 50, 82–85 *passim;* Mountains, 83, 84; River, 50, 51, 82, 83, 86, 87, 135
Kuskulana Glacier, 33
Kuzitrin flats, 106

Lake Aleknagik, 87
Lake Chakachamma, 50
Lake Clark, 50
Lake Norutak, 114
Lake Nutuyukti, 114, 117
Lake Peter, 114, 117, 121
Lake Schrader, 114, 117, 121
Lake Selby, 114, 117
Lake Takahula, 117
Lake Walker, 114
Lamplugh Glacier, 17

La Perouse Glacier, 25
Liberty Falls, 37
Lignite, 59; Creek, 59
Lisianski Inlet, 17
Little Delta River, 52, 55, 57
Little Diomede, 128
Little Sitkin, 72
Little Susitna River, 42
Lituya Bay, 21, 27, 28, 29
Livengood Creek, 101; gold camp, 91, 92, 100, 101, 115
Long, 86
Lost River, 107
Lynn Canal, 11, 12, 17; –Chatham Strait trough, 21

McCarthy Creek, 32
McCulloch Peak, 74
McGrath, 83, 86
McKinley Park: Highway, 52, 56, 58, 60; Hotel, 58; Station, 52, 58, 60
Magcik volcano, 71, 72
Malaspina Glacier, 25, 28, 29
Mancha Creek, 116
Manley Hot Springs, 93, 97, 99
Mansfield Peninsula, 10
Marmion Island, 16
Marsh Mountain, 87
Marshall, 85
Martin volcano, 71, 72
Matanuska: River, 40, 44, 46; Valley, 4, 6, 19, 38, 40, 42, 44, 45
Meier's Roadhouse, 35
Melozitna River, 90, 97, 99
Mendenhall: Glacier, 10, 17; Lake, 17
Mentasta: Mountains, 53, 57; Pass, 50, 53, 54; Valley, 37
Metcalf Cone, 74
Metlakahtla, 15
Middleton Island, 28
Midway Lake, 101
Miller House, 101
Minto Lakes, 99
Montague Island, 28
Moses Point, 106
Mount Allen, 54
Mount Atuk, 129
Mount Augusta, 21
Mount Blackburn, 31
Mount Chamberlin, 112, 114, 117
Mount Cook, 21
Mount Deborah, 49, 52, 57
Mount Doonerak, 112
Mount Drum, 31
Mount Edgecumbe, 14, 18
Mount Eielson, 57

Mount Fairplay, 102
Mount Fairweather, 9, 14, 17, 20
Mount Fellows, 58
Mount Foraker, 49, 57
Mount Gerdine, 49, 50
Mount Hague, 72
Mount Hayes, 49, 51, 52, 56, 57
Mount Hubbard, 20
Mount Hunter, 49, 57, 58
Mount Katmai, 70, 71. *See also* Katmai
Mount Kimball, 49, 53
Mount Logan, 20
Mount McKinley, 7, 29, 48, 49, 50, 51, 52, 57, 58; National Park, 34, 49, 50, 52, 55–56; North Peak, 51
Mount Marcus Baker, 22
Mount Michelson, 112
Mount Miller, 22
Mount Oratio, 84
Mount Osborn, 105
Mount St. Elias, 20, 21, 29
Mount Sanford, 31
Mount Schwatka, 93
Mount Spurr, 48, 49, 50, 61; –Mount Gerdine group, 49
Mount Steller, 22
Mount Tom White, 22
Mount Vancouver, 20
Mount Waskey, 84
Mount Witherspoon, 22
Mount Wrangell, 30, 31, 33
"Mud Mountain," 35
Muldrow Glacier, 51, 57, 60

Nabesna, 33; River, 33, 49, 53, 79
Naknek Lakes, 69
Nation River, 94
Nelson Island, 128, 135
Nenana: coal field, 52, 58, 60; Glacier, 57; gravel, 59; River, 38, 46, 49, 52, 56, 59, 60; town, 92
New Bogoslof Island, 74
Nichols Passage, 15
Nigu: Lake, 114; River, 114
Nimiuktuk River, 114, 115
Nizina Glacier, 32
Noatak River, 112, 114, 115, 117
Nome, 85, 99, 104, 106, 107, 108; River, 107, 110
Northway, 79, 92
Norton: Bay, 85, 106; highlands, 82, 83; Sound, 82, 105
Novarupta, 69, 70, 71
Nuka River, 115, 126
Nunivak Island, 128, 131, 135–136; National Wildlife Refuge, 136

Nushagak River, 82
Nutzotin Mountains, 4, 20, 53, 54, 56, 57
Nuvakuk River, 84
Nyac, 86

Ocean Point, 127
Okalee Spit, 28
Okmok caldera, 68
Okpilak River, 115
Old Bogoslof Island, 74
Old John Lake, 96, 114
Olnes, 100
Omilak, 107
Ophir, 86
Orange Creek, 94
Osviak River, 84
Otter Island, 132, 133

Palmer, 42
Panhandle, 9, 11, 20
Panorama Mountain, 56
Passage Canal, 22
Pavlof volcano, 63
Paxson, 34
Pedro Dome, 101
Peters Hills, 51
Petersburg, 10
Philip Smith Mountains, 112
Pilgrim: Hot Springs, 109, 110; River, 110
Pinnacle Island, 131, 132
Point Agassiz area, 10
Point Barrow, 115, 123, 125
Point Campbell, 43
Point Hey, 28
Point Hope, 123, 125, 126
Point Lay, 123, 125, 126
Point Retreat, 10
Poko Mountains, 120
Polychrome Pass, 58, 60
Poorman, 86
Porcupine River, 89, 93, 95, 97
Port Clarence, 105
Port Frederick, 12
Portage, 22; Creek, 115
Potter, 24, 26
Preacher Creek, 99
Pribilof Islands ("Amig"), 128, 131, 132–135
Prince of Wales Island, 10, 12
Prince William Sound, 22, 24, 26, 28

Rainbow, 26
Rainy Pass, 49, 50, 57
Rampart, 90, 91, 97; –Livengood area, 93
Ray Mountains, 91, 100
Red Bluff Bay, 18
Red Devil Mine, 87

Red Mountain, 86
Revillagigedo Island, 10, 11
Richardson: Highway, 24, 34, 35, 38, 49, 53, 55, 60, 80, 91, 101; Mountains, 112; Roadhouse, 101
Roberts Mountain, 136
Robertson River, 101
Robinson Mountains, 25
Rocky Mountains, 7, 9, 112
Romanzof Mountains, 111, 112
Roughtop Mountain, 93
Ruby, 86, 99
Russian Mountains, 83
Ruth Glacier, 50, 58

Sable: Mountain, 58; Pass, 58, 60
Sadlerochit: Mountains, 112, 126; River, 115
Sagavanirktok River, 112, 115, 126
St. Elias: Mountains, 6, 14, 19–27 *passim*, 48, 79, 102; province, 20. *See also* Mount St. Elias
St. George Island, 132, 133
St. Lawrence Island, 128, 129–131
St. Matthew Island, 128, 131–132
St. Michael, 85, 99
St. Paul Island, 132, 133, 135
Salcha River, 89, 92, 98
Salt Lake (Imuruk Basin), 105, 106, 109
Savonoski, 69; -Katmai trail, 69
Savoogna, 129, 130
Sawtooth Mountains, 93
Schwatka Mountains, 112, 114
Sealion Rock, 132
Segula, 72
Seldovia, 26
Semisopochnoi, 68, 72
Serpentine Hot Springs, 109
Seward, 22; Peninsula, 4, 5, 6, 76, 82, 83, 104–110; Railroad, 110
Shainin Lake, 114, 116
Shaw Creek, 98
Sheenjek River, 95, 115
Sheep River, 41
Shelikof Strait, 19, 69
Ship Rock (Sail Rock), 73, 74
Shishaldin volcano, 63
Shublik Mountains, 112, 126
Siksikpuk River, 123
Sitka, 14, 18
Skagway, 9, 11
Skull Cliff, 126
Skwentna River, 50, 57
Sledge Island, 128
Sleetmute, 87
Smith Bay, 125

Snake River, 107
Solomon, 106
Steese Highway, 91, 92, 99, 101
Stephens Passage, 16, 18
Stevens Village, 115
Stolby Rocks, 130
Stony River, 50
Strelna, 33
Sugar Mountain, 58
Summit Lake, 116
Sunshine Mountains, 83
Susitna: Glacier, 46, 47, 52; River, 36, 44, 46, 52; Valley, 38, 43, 44, 51

Tahoma Peak, 74
Taku, 10
Talkeetna, 51; Mountains, 4, 34, 38–42, 44–47 *passim;* River, 41
Tanacross, 80, 92
Tanaga: Island, 63; volcano, 63
Tanana: River, 33, 46, 49, 53, 79, 80, 82, 88, 89, 91, 92, 98, 101, 102; Valley, 54, 80, 102; town, 90, 99; -Kuskokwim lowland, 51
Tatalina River, 100
Tatonduk: River, 94; -Eagle area, 94
Taylor: Bay, 17; Highway, 91, 98, 102; Mountains, 83
Tazlina River, 36
Teller, 106
Tenderfoot Creek, 101
Tetling River, 55
Thorofare Pass, 56
Tikchik: Mountains, 84, 85; River, 84
Tingmerkpuk Mountains, 120
Tofty-Eureka, 91, 93
Togiak: Glacier, 84, 85; River, 84
Tok: flat, 79; Junction, 34, 92; River, 53, 80
Tokachitna Glacier, 50, 58
Tokatna, 86
Toklat River, 56, 59; East Fork of, 58
Tolovana, 93
Tonsina, 24, 34
Totemland, 13, 14
Tozitna River, 99
Tracy Arm, 10, 15
Trident volcano, 71, 72
Triumvirate Glacier, 50
Tulugak Lake, 116, 126
Turnagain Arm, 22, 26, 43, 44, 46, 47

Ukak, 69
Umiat, 120, 124, 127; Mountain, 123, 124, 127
Umnak Island, 63, 68, 73, 128
Unalaska, 73, 74, 132
Utukok River, 114, 121, 127

Valdez, 24, 26; Creek, 56
Valley of Ten Thousand Smokes, 69, 70
Vsevidof volcano, 63, 72

Wainwright, 123, 125, 126
Walakpai Lagoon, 125
Walker Lake, 117
Wall Street, 102
Walrus Island, 132, 133
Washington Creek, 100
White: Hills, 121; Mountains, 92; River, 49
Whitehorse, 54
Wild: Lake, 114; River, 115
Will Rogers and Wiley Post Memorial, 125
Willow Creek, 42
Windy, 52, 55, 56, 58
Wiseman mines, 95
Wolverine Mountain, 93

Wonder Lake, 60
Wood: Canyon, 37; River, 57, 59, 84; Wood
    River Mountains, 85
Wrangell Mountains, 5, 6, 19, 20, 30–33, 34,
    48, 54

Yakatoga district, 25, 27
Yakobi Island, 10, 17
Yakutat Bay, 21, 22, 24, 25, 28, 29
Yanert Glacier, 51, 53, 56, 57
York Mountains, 105, 106, 107
Yukon: Flats, 93, 95, 99, 100; River, 23, 29,
    49, 82, 85, 86, 88–91 *passim*, 93, 97, 98,
    100, 101, 115; -Innoko River, 82; -Kusko-
    kwim delta, 29, 81, 82, 135; -Tanana re-
    gion, 91, 92, 93, 99

Zarembo Island, 10, 11